Contents

C000225665

Introduction

The Abacus model

The Abacus materials are designed and written to allow for a daily, structured mathematics lesson:

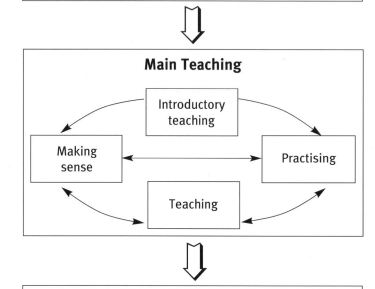

Mental Warm-up Activities
- Rehearsing previously-taught strategies
- Counting
- Number facts

Main Teaching

Introductory teaching

Making sense

Practising

Teaching

Plenaries
- Reinforcing key skills
- Addressing common difficulties
- Concluding with feedback or an activity

Each day's teaching begins with a whole class mental maths activity. These are presented in the **Mental Warm-up Activities** book.

The main part of the lesson is supported by the **Teacher Cards**:

- the front of each card gives support for whole class teaching for the first day of a topic
- the back of each card gives advice on further teaching for subsequent days and references to the practical activities included in this book. References to relevant **Workbook** pages and **Photocopy Masters** are also provided.

Each lesson is rounded-off with a plenary session. Guidance on key points to reiterate, common misconceptions to look out for, and whole class activities is included on the back of each Teacher Card.

Activity Book

The activities in this book are intended as follow-up to the introductory teaching. Each unit of the programme is supported by a range of activities covering different styles, numbers of children, resources etc.

Each activity includes the following information:

- Appropriate number of children, e.g. pairs, 3-4 children, whole class.

- A list of relevant materials. Any 'specialist' resources, e.g. number grids, number tracks ... are provided as Photocopy Masters at the back of the book. Number lines, number cards, place-value cards etc. are supplied separately in the **Resource Bank**.

- Level of difficulty, indicated by the following codes:

  ● basic work

  ●● for all children

  ●●● enrichment and extension.

- Learning points are also provided, drawing on the teaching objectives from the Teacher Card. These learning points will assist the teacher in directing the group and making informal assessments. They are also useful as key points to highlight in the plenary session – it may be beneficial to give the children some points to consider when setting up the activity. This will give them a clear focus for the outcome of the activity and any key points they might raise in the plenary session.

Whole class work

Following the initial teaching input, it is often a useful strategy to carry out some immediate consolidation, with the whole class or large group, working on an appropriate activity. Many of the units include a whole class activity specifically written to support this strategy. Such activities are indicated by the icon:

We suggest that following the initial teaching input for the whole class activity, the children are arranged in pairs or small groups, and work independently for a short period exploring or consolidating their learning. These activities will sometimes lead into the plenary session, where the topic can be rounded-off with a discussion about what the children have learned, any difficulties they encountered etc.

Classroom management

When working with groups it is important to have a manageable number of groups (about four is ideal). It may be appropriate for one or two of those groups to be working from a Workbook or Photocopy Master page. You may decide to have more than one group working on the same activity concurrently. You should try to focus your attention on one or two groups, working intensively with them, directing, discussing, evaluating etc. The Abacus model assists management by ensuring that all the children are broadly working within the same topic, at the same time as providing differentiated work through the activities in this book and the Photocopy Masters.

The activities are written with enough detail covering resources and learning outcomes (as well as the description of the activities themselves) to allow any support staff to easily manage groups you are not working with directly.

ACTIVITY 1
Whole class, in pairs

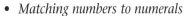

- *Matching numbers to numerals*
- *Reciting the number names to 20*

Number cards (1 to 20) one set per pair (PCMs 3, 4)

Count with the whole class. *One, two, three, four, five …* keeping a good pace. Say *Stop!* at a certain point. The children must find the card with that number on and hold it up. Repeat several times. Ask each pair to choose a number and to keep it secret. Recite the numbers slowly to the class. Any pair with a matching number should call it out and show you their card. Continue reciting slowly up to 20.

ACTIVITY 2
3-4 children

- *Matching numbers to numerals*
- *Reciting the number names to 20*

Blank number track (1 to 20) (PCM 2 – enlarged to A3), number cards (1 to 20) (PCMs 3, 4)

Shuffle the cards and lay them out face up on a table. The children help each other to lay them out along the track, starting with 1. They say the numbers as they lay them out. When they have completed the whole track, they count along it. Two or three children shut their eyes and one child removes a number. On opening their eyes, the children must say which number has been removed. Repeat this with the other children shutting their eyes.

ACTIVITY 3
3 children

- *Estimating a small number of objects*
- *Matching a number of objects to a numeral*

Cubes (or counters), number cards (1 to 20) (PCMs 3, 4)

Spread out the cards face up on the table. The first child takes two handfuls of counters. He estimates how many there are, then says the number out loud. The second child counts the cubes carefully. The third child matches the cubes with a card. Was the first child correct? Repeat, swapping roles.

ACTIVITY 4
3 children

- *Matching a number to a number of objects*
- *Matching a number to a numeral*

Card for labels ('one', 'two' … 'ten'), interlocking cubes, counters

Shuffle the cards and place them face down in a pile. Ask the children to build a series of towers, from one to ten cubes tall. They take turns to select a card and choose the matching tower, e.g. the tower of four cubes matches the 'four' card. At the end of each round the child with the tallest tower collects a counter. They play three rounds. The winner is the player with the most counters. Repeat the activity so that the player with the shortest tower collects a counter.

ACTIVITY 5
4 children

- *Matching numbers to numerals placing the numbers in order (1 to 20)*
- *Ordering numbers up to 20*

Number cards (1 to 20) (PCMs 3, 4)

Shuffle the cards and deal five to each player. One player starts by placing a card between 8 and 15, e.g. 11, face up on the table. The second player tries to place the number before or after that number, e.g. 10 or 12. If they can't go they knock the table and miss a turn. Continue until all the children have placed their cards. Repeat the activity.

N2 Ordering

ACTIVITY 1
Whole class, then 3 children

- *Recognising the number names (one to ten)*
- *Matching sets of objects to number names and vice versa*

Card (for number-name cards, one to ten), cubes

Spread out the cards face down on the table. Ask every child to hold up their hands with some fingers standing up and some folded down. Turn over a number-name card, e.g. two. Encourage the children to read the number together. *Two. Has anyone got two fingers standing up?* They must draw the number in the air and receive a cube. Repeat from the beginning. Continue until all the cards have been used. Who has more than three cubes?

ACTIVITY 2
3-4 children

- *Recognising the number names (one to ten)*

Number cards (1 to 10) (PCM 3), card (for number-name cards, one to ten)

Spread out the number-name cards face up. Shuffle the number cards and place them face down in a pile. The children take turns to pick a number card and match it to the correct number-name card, e.g. '3' matches 'Three'. When all the cards have been taken, they must check that they have matched them correctly and place them in order.

ACTIVITY 3
3-4 children

- *Recognising the number names (one to ten)*

Cards (for number-name cards, one to ten), a calculator

Spread out the cards face up. The children take turns to enter a number on the calculator between one and ten. The others find the matching number-name card and place it face down on the table. The children continue taking turns to enter a different number until all the cards have been matched.

ACTIVITY 4
2 children

- *Recognising the number names (one to ten)*

Infant Game 7: 'Star Crossed', 20 wooden bricks (10 of one colour and 10 of another)

(See instructions on the card.)

ACTIVITY 5
2 pairs

- *Recognising the number names (one to ten)*
- *Matching numerals to number names and vice versa*

Number cards (1 to 10) (PCM 3), card (for number-name cards, one to ten), counters

Shuffle each set of cards and place them face down in two piles. One pair turns over the top number card and the other pair turns over the top number-name card. All the children look at both cards. The pair with the highest number takes a counter. The children continue until all the cards have been turned over. Who has the most counters?

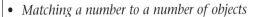

ACTIVITY 1
Whole class, in pairs

- *Matching a number to a number of objects*
- *Adding by counting two sets*

Number cards (1 to 20) one set per pair (PCMs 3, 4), 20 cubes, a dice
Each pair chooses a card less than 10. They match that number with cubes and build a tower. Throw the dice. The children take that number of cubes and build a second tower. They put both towers together to make one tall tower and work out how many cubes are in the tall tower. They hold up the matching number card and the card they first chose. Ask each pair to show their towers and say how many cubes there are. Repeat.

ACTIVITY 2
3-4 children

- *Matching a number to a number of objects*
- *Adding by counting two sets*

Four sets of number cards (1 to 12) (PCMs 3, 4), two dice
One child throws a dice and the others find the matching number card. A second child throws the second dice and the others find the matching card. They add the two numbers and find the card that matches the answer. They continue taking turns to throw the dice. Ask them to leave the cards out for you to check.

ACTIVITY 3
3-4 children

- *Matching a number to a number of objects*
- *Adding by counting two sets*

Number cards (1 to 12) (PCMs 3, 4), a set of dominoes
The children take a domino each. They count the number of spots on each side and add them together. They find a number card which matches the total and place the domino on the card, face up. Repeat several times. Some cards may have more than one domino placed on them. Which cards have more than two dominoes on them?

ACTIVITY 4
2-3 children

- *Matching a number to a number of objects*
- *Adding by counting two sets*

Number grid 1 (PCM 12), number cards (1 to 10) (PCM 3), a grid window (PCM 13), interlocking cubes
The children place the grid window so that it outlines two numbers on the grid. They collect an amount of cubes to match the total of the two numbers. E.g. for 5 and 4, they collect five cubes and four cubes making nine cubes in total. They select the number card which matches the total and place the two towers of cubes on the card. They continue outlining different numbers.

ACTIVITY 5
Pairs

- *Adding by counting two sets*

Concept keyboard with a word processor (create overlay and file to match)
The first child creates an addition using the pictures. The second child presses '=' and selects the answer from the numbers on the right of the keyboard. They take turns to write the additions or decide the answers.

♥ 1	🏠🏠 2	🌸🌸🌸 3	=	6	2	3
🌲🌲🌲 4			+	4	5	7

N4 Addition

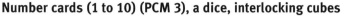

ACTIVITY 1
Whole class in pairs

- *Matching numbers to numerals*
- *Adding by counting on in ones*

Number cards (1 to 10) (PCM 3), a dice, interlocking cubes
Each pair takes a card. Throw a dice and write three numbers on the board (1 to 10) e.g. 3, 7, 9. Each pair adds the dice number to the card they chose. If the total matches a number on the board, they can say *Spot-on!* and receive a cube. The children return their card, choose another and you throw the dice again. Write three different numbers on the board. Repeat until everyone has a cube.

ACTIVITY 2
2 pairs

- *Matching numbers to sets of objects*
- *Adding by counting on in ones*
- *Adding numbers starting with the largest*

Several sets of number cards (1 to 20) (PCM 3, 4), card (to make '+' and '=' cards), interlocking cubes
One pair makes an addition choosing two numbers (up to 10). They lay it out using the cards, placing the largest number first, e.g. '8 + 5'. The other pair completes the addition using cards, i.e. '= 13'. The first pair checks the answer using cubes. Repeat several times allowing the children to swap roles. Extend by starting with three numbers to add.

ACTIVITY 3
3-4 children

- *Matching numbers to sets of objects*
- *Adding by counting on in ones*

Number cards (1 to 10) (PCM 3), interlocking cubes, a dice
Shuffle the cards and place them face down in a pile. One child takes a card. Another throws the dice and adds the number thrown to the number on the card. The other children use the cubes to check the answer. They place the total number of cubes and the card together. Repeat the activity, swapping roles.

ACTIVITY 4
2-3 children

- *Adding three numbers by counting on*
- *Reasoning about numbers and organising ideas*

Blank number grid (PCM 16), three sets of number cards (4, 5, 6) (PCM 3)
Ask the children to lay out the cards on the grid so that each row and each column adds up to 15. This is harder than it seems. If they succeed, they can use a 4 × 4 blank grid and lay out four sets of cards (3, 4, 5 and 6), so that each row and each column adds up to 18.

ACTIVITY 5
Pairs

- *Creating simple additions with answers*

Concept keyboard with a word processor (create overlay and file to match)
The first child creates an addition using the numbers on the left, starting with a larger number. The second selects the answer from the numbers on the right of the keyboard. They take turns to write additions or decide the answers.

4		3		2	5
			+	8	3
	1			4	10
			+	6	9
2		5		1	7

ACTIVITY 6
3 children

- *Adding two numbers by counting on (up to 14)*

Infant game 8: 'Dragon totals', a dice, counters (one colour per child)
(See instructions on the card.)

ACTIVITY 1
Whole class, in pairs

- *Matching a number to a set of objects*
- *Subtracting by taking away*
A dice, interlocking cubes
Each pair builds a tower of between six and twelve cubes. Write the numbers 1, 2, 3, 4, 5, 6 on the board. Throw a dice. Ask the children to take away a matching number of cubes from their tower. Any pair with a tower matching one of the numbers on the board can say *Spot-on!* and receives a cube. Repeat until every pair has a cube.

ACTIVITY 2
3-4 children

- *Subtracting by taking away*
Number cards (1 to 20) (PCMs 3, 4), interlocking cubes
Shuffle the cards and spread them out face down. One child turns over two cards, e.g. 8 and 3. Together, the children subtract the smaller number from the larger, i.e. 8 take away 3. They may use their fingers to help. They count out the number of cubes to match the answer, i.e. five, and place the two cards and the cubes together. Check their subtraction. Continue until all the cards are turned over.

ACTIVITY 3
3-4 children

- *Counting objects up to 10*
- *Subtracting by taking away*
Number cards (1 to 10) (PCM 3), card (to make '−' and '=' cards) interlocking cubes, a feely bag
The children count eight cubes into the bag. One child removes a small number of cubes and shows the others, e.g. two. The other children say how many are left in the bag. They check by counting out the cubes. If they are correct they set out the subtraction using the number cards and the sign cards. Continue, with the children swapping roles several times.

ACTIVITY 4
2-3 children

- *Subtracting by taking away*
- *Recognising difference as subtraction*
Blank 2 × 2 grid (drawn on a large sheet of paper), two sets of number cards (3 to 7) (PCM 3)
The children lay out the cards on the grid, so that the difference between each pair of numbers along each side (rows and columns) is exactly two. How many ways can they find to do this? E.g.

6	4
4	2

3	5
1	3

ACTIVITY 5
Pairs

- *Subtracting by taking away*
Concept keyboard with a word processor (create overlay and file to match)
The first child creates a subtraction using the pictures and the numbers in the right hand column. The second child presses '=' and selects the answer. They take turns to write the subtractions or decide the answers.

							=	3
♡	🏠	🏠	🌼🌼🌼	🎈🎈				1
1	2		3					2
🌳🌳🌳		🍎🍎🍎	🎈🎈				−	4
4		5	6					5

N6 Money

ACTIVITY 1
Whole class, in pairs

- *Recognising coins*

A set of coins (1p, 2p, 5p, 10p, 20p, 50p, £1)

Give each pair two coins. Call out a description, e.g. *Brown and round*. Do any of the pairs have a coin which matches that description? If so, they must say what the coin is. Draw the appropriate coins on the board. Then call out another description. Which coin is it? Repeat several times.

ACTIVITY 2
3-4 children

- *Recognising coins*

A set of coins (1p, 2p, 5p, 10p, 20p, 50p, £1), a feely bag

Place the coins in the bag. The children take turns to feel for a coin, say what they think it is, and then remove it from the bag. If they are correct, they keep it. Otherwise they replace it in the bag. They continue until all the coins have been collected. The winner is the player with most coins.

ACTIVITY 3
3-4 children

- *Matching two identical coins*
- *Recognising coins*

A set of coins (1p, 2p, 5p, 10p, 20p, 50p, £1), a feely bag

Place the coins in the bag. The children take turns to feel in the bag and remove a coin. The coin is replaced each time. The winner is the first player to recognise and remove the same coin three times.

ACTIVITY 4
3-4 children

- *Recognising coins*
- *Understanding the value of different coins*

Two sets of coins (1p, 2p, 5p, 10p, 20p, 50p), a feely bag

Put the coins in the bag and shake it up. Each child takes out a coin without showing the others. When they all have a coin they open their hands together and compare coins. The person with the most valuable coin keeps it. The rest of the coins are put back in the bag and shaken up. They continue until all the coins have gone.

ACTIVITY 5
2-3 children

- *Making up amounts using different coins*
- *Adding sets of coins*

A set of coins (1p, 2p, 5p, 10p), number cards (1 to 20) (PCMs 3, 4), interlocking cubes

Shuffle the cards and place them in a pile face down. The children each take a card. They take coins to match the number on the card. The others check they are correct. If so, they take a cube. They continue, taking a different card each, until all the cards have gone.

ACTIVITY 1
Whole class, in pairs

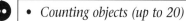

- *Counting objects (up to 20)*
- *Recognising that the number of objects is equal to the last number spoken*
- *Grouping objects in twos in order to count accurately*

20 interlocking cubes, 20 raisins and 20 pencils; tray (or paper plates)

Place a pile of cubes, raisins and pencils on a tray or separate paper plates. The children have to write down an estimate for the number of objects in each set (up to 20). When everyone has written down their estimate, ask each pair to swap their paper with the pair next to them. Count out the objects in each set, grouping the items in twos as you go. Write down the actual number. Who had the closest guess?

ACTIVITY 2
3 children

- *Counting*
- *Reciting the number names in order*
- *Placing the numbers in order (from 1 to 20)*

Number cards (1 to 20) (PCMs 3, 4)

Shuffle the cards and place them face down in a pile. One child takes a card and places it face up on the table. The next child takes a card and places it alongside the first card – to the left, if it is smaller, or to the right if the number is larger. Continue until all the cards have been sorted, then lay them out in order from left to right.

ACTIVITY 3
3-4 children

- *Counting*
- *Reciting the number names in order*
- *Placing the numbers in order from (1 to 20)*

Number cards (1 to 20) (PCMs 3, 4)

Place the cards face up in a line in order (1 to 20). One child turns six cards face down, while the others close their eyes. They open their eyes and take turns to point to a card, say what they think the number is and turn it over to see if they are correct. They repeat the activity several times, swapping roles.

ACTIVITY 4
3-4 children

- *Estimating a number of objects and checking by counting*

1p coins, a feely bag

Put the coins in the bag and shake it up. The children take turns to remove a handful of coins. They count them out without letting the others know how much money they have. They write down three numbers: the number for the amount of coins they have, plus any two other numbers. In turn, each child flashes their handful of money and shows the others their three numbers. They have to guess which is the correct number for the amount of coins. The other children check each amount as it is revealed.

ACTIVITY 5
2-3 children

- *Counting objects (up to 20)*
- *Grouping to count*

1p coins, number cards (1 to 20) (PCMs 3, 4), interlocking cubes

Shuffle the cards and place them in a pile face down. The children each take a card. They must take enough cubes to match the number on the card. The others check if they are correct. If they are, they take a coin. The children continue, taking a different card each, until all the cards have gone.

N8 Counting in twos

ACTIVITY 1
Whole class, in pairs

- *Counting in twos from (2 to 20)*
Three sets of even number cards (2 to 20) (PCMs 3, 4), interlocking cubes
Shuffle the cards and give out one to each pair. Begin to count in twos from 2 to 20, and stop on the way. Repeat the last number spoken. Any pair with that card can take a cube. Continue on up to 20 and stop again. Start at 2 again and stop in a different place. Continue until every pair has a cube.

ACTIVITY 2
3 children

- *Matching numbers to numerals*
- *Matching numbers to sets of objects*
- *Counting in twos (from 2 to 20)*
Number cards (2 to 20) (PCMs 3, 4), interlocking cubes
The children lay out the cards in order. Ask them to separate out the twos, i.e. two, four … (from 2 to 20). They lay these cards in a line and put the rest away. Ask them to build a tower of cubes to match each number and arrange the towers in order. What do they notice about the towers?

ACTIVITY 3
4 children

- *Matching numbers to numerals*
- *Counting in twos (from 2 to 20)*
Two sets of even number cards (2 to 20) (PCMs 3, 4)
The children shuffle the cards and deal out five each. One child starts by laying down 2. The next child can play if she can lay down 4. If not, she knocks on the table and play passes to the next child. They continue until one child has no cards left. Repeat, starting with a different child.

ACTIVITY 4
3-4 children

- *Matching numbers to numerals*
- *Counting in twos (from 2 to 20)*
Number cards (1 to 10) (PCM 3), interlocking cubes
Spread out the cards face up on the table. The children lay them in a line (1 to 10). They turn over every other card, starting with the 1, and build towers to match the cards facing up.

ACTIVITY 5
2-3 children

- *Matching even numbers to sets of 2p coins*
- *Counting in twos (from 2 to 20)*
Ten 2p coins, number cards (1 to 10) (PCM 3)
Shuffle the cards and place them in a pile face down. The children each take a card and match the number on the card with the same number of 2p coins. Together, they work out the total value they each have and write down the amount. E.g. they take the card 4 and so they take four 2p coins. They work out that they have 8p. Repeat several times.

N9 Place-value

ACTIVITY 1
Whole class, then 3-4 children

- *Saying a 'teen' number based on tens and units*
Coins (one 10p, nine 1ps), number cards (1 to 20) (PCMs 3, 4), a feely bag
Place the coins in the bag. The children take turns to remove a few coins. The other children find a number card which matches the amount of money they have. Check the coins and card match. Replace the coins in the bag and play again.

ACTIVITY 2
3-4 children

- *Converting a number into tens and units (up to 20)*
Number cards (10 to 20) (PCMs 3, 4), interlocking cubes
The children make a tower of ten cubes. Shuffle the cards and spread them out, face down. The children take turns to choose a card, not allowing the others to see. They must match the number with cubes, using the tower of ten and other cubes. The other children have to say what the number is. The child reveals the card.

ACTIVITY 3
3 children

- *Converting a number into tens and units (up to 20)*
Number cards (1 to 20) (PCMs 3, 4), coins (1p, 10p)
Shuffle the cards, and place them face down in a pile. The children take one card each, and match it with coins, using a 10p coin if the number is ten or more. The children look at each other's sets of money and check that they match the cards. The child who has collected the most money keeps all three cards. Replace the money and play again. After six rounds, who has collected the most cards?

ACTIVITY 4
3 children

- *Converting a number into tens and units (up to 30)*
- *Collecting units, and exchanging ten units for a ten*
Number cards (10 to 30) (PCMs 3 to 5), Base Ten equipment (tens and ones)
Each child takes two cards, and matches each number with the Base Ten material, using tens and ones. They check each other's. Each child puts their two Base Ten numbers together and exchanges ones for tens, if possible. Compare each child's total. Who has the most? Who has the least? The children replace the material and repeat.

ACTIVITY 5
3-4 children

- *Matching 10p and 1p coins to numbers up to 20*
Infant game 9: 'Coin Collector', counters, coins (1p, 10p)
(See instructions on the card.)

N10 Subtraction

ACTIVITY 1
Whole class, in pairs

• *Matching numbers to numerals*
• *Subtracting from a number by counting back*
Number cards (2 to 20) (PCMs 3, 4)
Shuffle the cards and place them in a pile face down. Choose a pair of children.
Give them a card from the top of the pile, e.g. 14. They have to say the number
which is two less, i.e. 12. They replace the card on the bottom of the pile and
take another card from the top. They choose a new pair of children and give
them the card. Keep playing until all the cards have been used.

ACTIVITY 2
2-3 children

• *Matching numbers to numerals*
• *Subtracting from a number by counting back*
**Number grid 2 (PCM 14), blank grid (PCM 16), pencils, number track (1 to 10)
(PCM 1)**
The children take away two from every number on the grid. They write the
answers in the matching spaces on the blank grid. Use the number track to
check subtractions.

ACTIVITY 3
3-4 children

• *Matching numbers to numerals*
• *Subtracting from a number by counting back*
• *Matching numbers to sets of objects*
**Two sets of number cards (3 to 10) (PCM 3), a dice (numbered 1, 2, 3 twice),
interlocking cubes, number track (1 to 10) (PCM 1)**
Shuffle the cards and place them face down in a pile. The children take turns to
turn over a card and throw the dice. They subtract the dice number from the
card number and collect cubes to match the answer. The winner is the first
person to collect 25 cubes. Use the number track to check subtractions.

ACTIVITY 4
3-4 children

• *Subtracting from a number by counting back*
• *Recognising number pairs to 10*
Number track (1 to 10) (PCM 1), number cards (1 to 10) (PCM 3), counters
Shuffle the cards and place them face down in a pile. The children take turns to
reveal a card. They take that number away from ten and place a counter on the
matching number on the track. E.g. a child turns over 4 and takes four away
from ten, leaving six. She places a counter on the 6 on the grid. The card is
returned to the bottom of the pile. Continue until all the numbers are covered.

ACTIVITY 5
2-3 children

• *Counting back one and two*
• *Matching numbers to numerals*
Number track (1 to 10) (PCM 1), counters, a coin
Ask the children to put all the counters on 10 on
the number track. They take turns to toss a coin.
If it lands 'heads', the child moves his counter
back one. If it lands 'tails', he moves his counter
back two. However, the child has to say what
number he will land on before he moves his
counter. The first person to reach 1 wins.

ACTIVITY 6
3 children

• *Taking away the smaller of two numbers (up to 10)*
Infant game 10: 'Flying Kites', 14 wooden bricks, calculator
(See instructions on the card.)

N11 Addition

ACTIVITY 1
Whole class, in pairs

- *Recognising the relationship between addition and subtraction*

Number cards (1 to 10) (PCM 3) one set per pair, card (for '+', '–' and '=' cards)

The children make an addition or subtraction using three of their number cards. Give them five minutes to work one out and then choose a pair to write it on the board, e.g. '4 + 5 = 9'. *Can anyone think of a subtraction using the same numbers?* E.g. '9 – 4 = 5'. Choose another pair to write on the board. Repeat.

ACTIVITY 2
2-3 children

- *Recognising addition pairs to 5*
- *Matching numbers to sets of objects*

Three sets of number cards (0 to 5) (PCM 3), interlocking cubes

Using no more than two colours, the children build as many different towers from five cubes as they can. E.g. five red cubes and no blue cubes, four red cubes and one blue cube. Ask them to lay out number cards to match each tower, e.g. '5 and 0', '4 and 1'. Repeat using three cubes of two different colours.

ACTIVITY 3
2 pairs

- *Matching coins to amounts*
- *Recognising addition pairs to 5 (and 6) using coins*

Coins (1p, 2p, 5p)

In their pairs, the first child uses any coins to make five pence, e.g. two 2p coins and a 1p coin. The second child makes five pence using different coins, e.g. one 5p. Continue until they have found all four ways. They write additions for each set. Repeat making six pence.

ACTIVITY 4
2-3 children

- *Matching coins to amounts*
- *Adding coins to make 10p*

Coins (1p, 2p, 5p, 10p)

The children use the coins to find as many ways as they can to make 10p. They write an addition for each one, e.g. '2p + 2p + 1p + 5p = 10p'.

ACTIVITY 5
2 pairs

- *Recognising addition pairs to 5*
- *Matching numbers to sets of objects*

Number cards (1 to 5) (PCM 3), sets of beads, strings

Spread out the cards on the table. The children each take a card. In their pairs they thread beads onto a string (one child at each end of the string) to match their number, to make a total number. E.g. if they choose the numbers 3 and 5, they thread three red beads at one end of the string and five blue beads at the other. They count the total number of beads and write an addition to match each one. Each pair checks the other pair's addition. Replace the cards and repeat.

N12 Addition
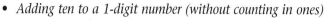

ACTIVITY 1
Whole class, in pairs

- *Adding ten to a 1-digit number (without counting in ones)*
Number cards (1 to 10) (PCM 3), card (for '+' and '=' cards)
Each pair writes three 'teen' numbers on their paper. Shuffle the cards and place them in a pile face down. One child takes a card and reads out the number and adds ten to it. Write the addition on the board. If any pair has the answer written as one of their three numbers, they may cross it out. Repeat, with other children taking a card and adding ten. The first pair to cross out all their numbers wins.

ACTIVITY 2
2-3 children

- *Adding ten to a 1-digit number (without counting in ones)*
- *Matching numbers to numerals*
Number cards (11 to 20) (PCM 4), counters (two or three colours), two dice (with the sixes covered)
Ask the children to arrange the cards in a row, from 11 to 20. Taking turns, the children throw one or two dice and count the dots. They add ten to the total and place a counter on the card to match their answer. If there is already a counter there, they take if off and replace it with their own. Repeat, until all the cards are covered by a counter. Who has most counters on the cards?

ACTIVITY 3
3-4 children

- *Matching coins to written amounts (up to 10p)*
- *Adding 10p to an amount*
Coins (1p, 2p, 5p, 10p), two sets of number cards (1 to 20) (PCMs 3, 4)
Each child takes an amount of money which totals less than 10p, then finds a matching number card, e.g. for two 2ps, the matching card is 4. They take turns to take a 10p coin and decide how much they now have, e.g. 14. Another child has to find the matching card. The others check if she is correct. Repeat, taking different amounts of money. The children should leave all the cards in pairs, the first number with its 'ten more' card.

ACTIVITY 4
2-3 children

- *Recognising numbers with a difference of ten*
Two sets of number cards (0 to 30) (PCMs 3 to 5)
Spread out the cards face down on the table. The children take turns to reveal three cards. If they turn over any two cards where one number is ten more than the other, they keep that pair of cards and the third card is turned back over. If not, all the cards are turned back over. Repeat until most of the cards have been taken. Who has the most pairs?

ACTIVITY 5
2-3 children

- *Recognising numbers with a difference of one*
- *Matching numbers to numerals*
Two sets of number cards (1 to 10) (PCM 3)
Spread out the cards face down on the table. The children take turns to reveal two cards. If they turn over a pair of cards which are adjacent numbers (where one number is one more than the other), they keep that pair of cards. If not, the cards are turned face down again. They continue until most of the cards have been taken. Who has the most pairs?

ACTIVITY 1
Whole class, in pairs

- *Adding sets of coins to make 10p*
- *Recognising coins*
- *Reasoning about numbers*

Coins (1p, 2p, 5p)
Ask each pair to think of a way of making 10p using smaller value coins. They should try to think of an unusual way. Give them five minutes to think about it and then discuss the different ways: *Has anyone found a way which uses a 1p coin? ... a 2p coin?* etc. Write each different way on the board.

ACTIVITY 2
3-4 children

- *Adding sets of coins to make amounts*
- *Recognising coins*

A collection of objects (labelled 2p, 3p, ... 11p), coins (1p, 2p, 5p, 10p)
One child is the shopkeeper, the others are shoppers. Each shopper takes five of each coin. The shoppers take turns to buy something using exactly two coins to match the value of the item. The shopkeeper collects the money. The children should buy three items each. The items and coins are then returned and the activity is repeated with a different shopkeeper. Discuss which items they cannot buy with just two coins (5p, 8p, 9p).

ACTIVITY 3
3-4 children

- *Adding sets of coins to make amounts*
- *Recognising coins*

A collection of objects (labelled 1p, 2p, ... 12p), coins (1p, 2p, 5p, 10p), a feely bag
Place the coins in the bag. One child is the shopkeeper, the others are shoppers. Each shopper takes five coins from the bag. The shoppers take turns to buy something from the shop by handing over the correct amount to the shopkeeper, who collects the money. They try to buy three items each. The children return the items and the coins and the activity is repeated with a different shopkeeper.

ACTIVITY 4
2-3 children

- *Adding sets of coins to make amounts*
- *Reasoning about numbers and organising ideas*

Coins (2p, 5p, 10p), number cards (1 to 20) (PCMs 3, 4)
Spread out the cards face up on the table. The children have to work together to decide which card numbers they can make using the coins they have, bearing in mind that they do not have any 1ps. Which numbers are impossible to make?

ACTIVITY 5
2-3 children

- *Adding sets of coins to make amounts*

Card for labels ('1p' ... '10p'), coins (1p, 2p, 5p)
Shuffle the cards and place them face down in a pile. The children take turns to reveal the top card and place one, two or three coins on it to match the price exactly.

(N14) Addition

ACTIVITY 1
Whole class, in pairs

• *Recognising number pairs which total ten*
Blank domino cards (PCM 21), number cards (1 to 10) (PCM 3), felt-tipped pens, interlocking cubes
Each pair has to draw a domino with a total number of ten spots. Once they have decided what their domino is to look like, they can colour in the spots. Give them five minutes to do this. Shuffle the number cards and place them in a pile face down. Take a card and read out the number. *Does any pair have this number on one side of their domino?* If so, they have to shout out the number on the other side. If they do this correctly, they may take a cube. Keep turning over the cards and checking the dominoes.

ACTIVITY 2
4 children

• *Recognising number pairs which total ten*
Four sets of number cards (0 to 10) (PCM 3)
Shuffle the cards and spread them out face down. The children play 'Pelmanism'. They take turns to reveal two cards. If the cards add up to ten, they keep them. Otherwise, they turn the cards back over. Play continues until all the pairs have been taken.

ACTIVITY 3
3 children

• *Matching numbers to sets of objects*
• *Recognising number pairs which total 10*
Number cards (0 to 10) (PCM 3), interlocking cubes
Spread out the cards face up. One child lays out ten cubes in a row. The others shut their eyes and the first child removes some cubes from the row. When the children open their eyes, they must select the card that matches the number of cubes removed. The first child then replaces the cubes, counting them as he does so. Were they correct? The children continue taking turns to remove the cubes. Repeat with rows of different lengths.

ACTIVITY 4
2-3 children

• *Recognising sets of numbers which total 10*
• *Reasoning about numbers and organising ideas*
Number cards (1 to 9) (PCM 3)
Using the number cards, how many ways can the children find to make ten, by adding? For example, they could add 1 + 2 + 3 + 4. What other ways are there of making ten?

ACTIVITY 5
2-3 children

• *Recognising number pairs which total 10*
A set of dominoes
How many dominoes can the children find which have a total of ten spots? How many can they find which have less than ten spots? How many have more than ten?

ACTIVITY 6
2-3 children

• *Recognising different sets of coins which make the same amount*
Coins (1p, 2p, 5p, 10p)
Explore different ways of making 10p, placing sets of coins in rows. How many different ways are there? How many coins in each set? Change from 10p to a different amount, e.g. 8p or 12p.

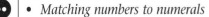

N15 Numbers to 100

ACTIVITY 1
Whole class, in pairs

- *Matching numbers to numerals*
- *Counting (from 1 to 30)*
- *Comparing two numbers*

Number grid (0 to 39) (PCM 17), counters, Blu-tack, interlocking cubes

Each pair chooses a number on the grid. They mustn't tell anyone which number they have chosen but they must remember it. Stick a counter on the grid on a number between 15 and 25. The children have to say what number is covered by the counter. They stand up if the number they have chosen is larger. Check that they are correct. Has anyone chosen the number covered? If so they get a cube. Repeat many times.

ACTIVITY 2
4-5 children

- *Counting (from 1 to 30)*
- *Matching numbers to numerals*

Number cards (1 to 30) (PCMs 3 to 5)

Shuffle the cards and place them face down in a pile. One child removes a card, places it face up on the table and says the number out loud, e.g. *Twenty-two*. The children then continue to count out loud, taking turns to say the next number *Twenty-three, twenty-four, twenty-five …* until they reach thirty. The child who says *Thirty* keeps the card. The children continue taking turns to pick a card and counting on, until one child has five cards.

ACTIVITY 3
3 children

- *Matching numbers to coins (1ps and 10ps)*
- *Recognising numerals and matching to numbers*

Number cards (1 to 30) (PCMs 3 to 5), coins (1p, 10p)

Shuffle the cards and place them face down in a pile. One child chooses a card, e.g. 14, and without showing it to the others, matches the number with coins, i.e. he takes one 10p and four 1p coins. The other children look at the coins and say which number is on the card. If they are correct, the card is placed to one side. Otherwise the card is returned to the bottom of the pile. The children continue taking turns to pick a card until all the cards have been used.

ACTIVITY 4
2-3 children

- *Ordering 2-digit numbers*
- *Recognising tens and units in 2-digit numbers*
- *Reasoning about numbers and organising ideas*

Number cards (1 to 9) (PCM 3)

How many 2-digit numbers can the children make using the number cards, e.g. 24 and 42, 19 and 91? What is the largest possible number they can make? (98.) What is the smallest? (12.) How many different numbers can the children make?

ACTIVITY 5
2-3 children

- *Matching numerals to numbers*
- *Ordering numbers (1 to 30)*
- *Counting (from 1 to 30)*

Number cards (1 to 20) (PCMs 3, 4), 2 × 10 blank grid (drawn on a large piece of paper)

Shuffle the cards and lay them face up on the table. The children take turns to take a card and place it in the correct box on the grid so that eventually it will look like the top two rows of the 1 to 100 number grid. The children continue, helping each other until all the cards are in the correct boxes on the grid. Repeat with individuals attempting on their own.

N16 Place-value

ACTIVITY 1
Whole class, then 3-4 children

- *Recognising a number as tens and ones (up to 30)*
Number cards (1 to 30) (PCMs 3 to 5), coins (two 10ps, nine 1ps), a feely bag
Place the coins in the bag. The children take turns to remove a few and add
them together. The other children find a matching number card. Check that
the coins and card match for each child. Ask the children to replace the coins
in the bag and play again.

ACTIVITY 2
3-4 children

- *Converting a number into tens and ones (up to 40)*
**Number cards (1 to 40) (PCMs 3 to 6), coins (1p and 10p), a book with at least
40 pages**
One child opens the book before page 40 and, without showing the others,
reads the page number out loud. The other children collect the matching
number of coins and find the matching number card. The first child shows
them the book. Do the numbers match? They place the card and the coins
together on the table. Repeat, swapping the different roles.

ACTIVITY 3
4 children

- *Converting a number into tens and ones (up to 30)*
- *Ordering numbers (between 10 and 30)*
- *Recognising the largest and smallest number*
**Number cards (10 to 30) (PCMs 3 to 5), interlocking cubes (some towers of ten
cubes and some loose), counters**
Shuffle the cards and place them face down in a pile. Each child picks a card
and takes towers and loose cubes to match the number. They compare numbers
and the child with the lowest number keeps his card and takes a counter. The
other cards are returned to the bottom of the pile. The children continue taking
cards and comparing cubes, until one of them has four counters.

ACTIVITY 4
4-5 children

- *Converting a number into tens and ones (up to 30)*
- *Reciting numbers, in sequence (from 1 to 30)*
Number cards (1 to 30) (PCMs 3 to 5), Base Ten equipment (tens and ones)
Shuffle the cards and place them face down in a pile. One child removes a card,
places it face up on the table and says the number out loud, e.g. *Twenty-two*.
The children continue to count out loud, taking turns to say the next number
Twenty-three, twenty-four, twenty-five ... until they reach thirty. The child who
says *Thirty* matches the original card with Base Ten equipment. If correct he
keeps the card. The children continue taking turns to pick a card and counting
on, until one of them has five cards.

ACTIVITY 5
3 children

- *Converting a 2-digit number into tens and ones (units)*
Number cards (10 to 50) (PCMs 3 to 6), Base Ten equipment (tens and ones)
Each child takes two cards and matches each number with the Base Ten
material, using tens and ones. Ask them to check each other's. Each child puts
his/her two Base Ten numbers together and exchanges ones for tens, if possible.
They compare numbers and amounts of Base Ten material. Who has the most?
Who has the least? Replace the material and repeat several times.

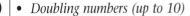

ACTIVITY 1
Whole class, in pairs

- *Doubling numbers (up to 10)*
- *Recognising the double of numbers (up to 10)*

Number cards (0 to 10 for the children, 1 to 20 even numbers only for the teacher) (PCMs 3, 4)

Each pair chooses four number cards and lays them out face up. Shuffle the even number cards and place them in a pile face down. Choose a child to take a card and ask him to read out the number. If any pair can double one of their numbers to match this number, they may turn over their number card. Repeat several times. The first pair to turn over all four cards wins.

ACTIVITY 2
4-5 children

- *Doubling numbers (up to 10)*
- *Recognising the double of numbers (up to 10)*

Two sets of number cards (1 to 20) (PCMs 3, 4), two sets of number cards (1 to 10) (PCM 3)

Spread out the cards face down on the table. The children take turns to reveal two cards. If they reveal a pair of cards in which one number is double the other, they keep the cards. If not, they turn the cards back over. The children continue until all the cards have been taken. Who has the most pairs?

ACTIVITY 3
3 children

- *Doubling numbers (up to 10) using cubes*

Number cards (1 to 10) (PCM 3), number cards (1 to 20) (PCMs 3, 4), interlocking cubes

Spread out the 1 to 20 number cards face up. Shuffle the 1 to 10 cards and place them in a pile face down. One child takes a card. He lays it down and reads the number. The second child builds a tower with a matching number of cubes. The third child has to build another tower the same size. The first child puts the two towers together to make one tall tower. They count how many cubes are in the tall tower and find the matching card from those face up on the table. The children put both cards and the tower together and start the activity again.

ACTIVITY 4
2-3 children

- *Doubling numbers (up to 20) using coins*

Number cards (10 to 20) (PCMs 3, 4), post-it notes, coins (1p, 2p)

Shuffle the cards and place them in a pile face down. The children take turns to take a card. They work together to calculate its double, using the coins if necessary. They write the double on a post-it note and stick it on the card. Repeat several times.

N18 Addition

ACTIVITY 1
Whole class, in pairs

• *Matching numbers to numerals*
• *Recognising addition pairs to make 6*
Number cards (0 to 6) (PCM 3), large number cards (0 to 6) (PCM 3 – enlarged to A3)
Each pair chooses four number cards to lay out face up. Shuffle the large number cards and place them in a pile face down. Choose a child to take a card and ask him to read out the number. If any pair has a number which, when added to his number makes six, they may turn over that number card. Repeat this several times. The first pair to turn over all their cards is the winner.

ACTIVITY 2
4-5 children

• *Recognising addition pairs to make 7*
Four sets of number cards (0 to 7) (PCM 3)
Spread out the cards face down on the table. The children take turns to reveal two cards. If they turn over a pair of cards which add up to seven, they can keep that pair of cards. If not, they turn the cards back over. The children play until most of the cards have been taken. Who has the most pairs?

ACTIVITY 3
4 children

• *Matching numbers to numerals*
• *Recognising addition pairs to make 6*
A set of dominoes
Share out the dominoes equally between the four children. The children take turns to place a domino on the table face up – the adjoining halves of each domino must add up to six. If a child cannot play, he must knock on the table and miss a turn. The children play until no one can go. Who has the most dominoes left? Repeat.

ACTIVITY 4
2-3 children

• *Matching numbers to sets of objects*
• *Recognising addition pairs to make 5*
Interlocking cubes (in two colours)
The children have to build towers five cubes tall using two colours, but each tower must be different. How many different towers can the children make? When they think they have made them all, ask them to group the towers according to the number of red and blue cubes in each one. Ask them to write the matching additions, e.g. '4 + 1 = 5'. Repeat for towers of six cubes.

ACTIVITY 5
2-3 children

• *Recognising sets of numbers which total 5*
• *Reasoning about numbers and systematising the findings*
Interlocking cubes (five colours)
The children have to build towers five cubes tall, but each tower must contain different numbers of coloured cubes. How many different towers can the children make? They should match each tower to an addition, e.g. if a tower has five different coloured cubes, it matches to '1 + 1 + 1 + 1 + 1 = 5'. Similarly, if a tower has one red cube, one blue cube and three green cubes, it matches to '1 + 1 + 3 = 5'. When they think they have made them all, they can order all the matching additions. When they have finished, let them repeat for towers of six cubes, using up to six colours.

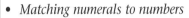

ACTIVITY 1
Wholeclass, in pairs

- *Matching numerals to numbers*
- *Recognising addition pairs to make 8*

Number cards (0 to 8) per pair (PCM 3), large number cards (0 to 8) (PCM 3 – enlarged to A3)

Each pair chooses four number cards to lay out face up. Shuffle the large number cards and place them in a pile face down. Choose a child to take a card and read out the number. If any pair has a number which, when added to his number, makes eight, they may turn over that number card. Repeat this several times. The first pair to turn over all their cards is the winner.

ACTIVITY 2
4-5 children

- *Matching numerals to numbers*
- *Recognising addition pairs to make 9*

Four sets of number cards (0 to 9) (PCM 3)

Spread out the cards face down on the table. The children take turns to reveal two cards. If they turn over a pair of cards which add up to nine, they keep that pair of cards. If not, they replace the cards face down. The children play until most of the cards have been taken. Who has the most pairs?

ACTIVITY 3
4 children

- *Matching totals to numbers*
- *Recognising addition pairs to make 10*

A set of dominoes

Spread out the dominoes face up. The children try to find **pairs** of dominoes with a total of ten spots, e.g. 1/1 and 4/4. How many pairs can they find? To extend the activity ask them to record each pair of dominoes by drawing around them and copying the spots, and then re-use the dominoes. Repeat for totals of eight and nine.

ACTIVITY 4
2-3 children

- *Matching numbers to objects*
- *Recognising addition pairs to make 10*

Interlocking cubes (red and blue)

Each child has to build a tower ten cubes tall using two colours. Each tower must be different but all the reds/blues in the tower should be together. How many different towers can the children make? When they think they have made them all, ask them to group the towers according to the number of red and blue cubes in each one. Ask them to write the matching additions, e.g. '4 + 6 = 10'.

ACTIVITY 5
3 children

- *Matching numbers to sets of objects*
- *Recognising addition pairs to make 10*

Ten 1p coins

The children place the coins on the table and take turns to pick some up whilst the others turn their backs. The other children count the remaining coins and say how many the first child picked up. Are they correct?

ACTIVITY 6
2-3 children

- *Recognising addition pairs to make 10*

Number grid 1 (PCM 12), counters, interlocking cubes (towers of ten)

The children cover all the numbers on the grid with counters. They take turns to remove a counter, read the number aloud and say the number that pairs with it to make ten. The others check using the towers of ten cubes. If correct the child collects the counter, if not they replace it. They continue until all the counters have been removed.

N20 **Addition**

ACTIVITY 1
Whole class, in pairs

- *Recognising addition pairs to make 10*
- *Adding three numbers*

Several sets of number cards (0 to 9) (PCM 3), interlocking cubes
Write a number between 10 and 20 on the board. Give one number card to each pair. Each pair tells you the number that pairs with their card to make ten. If they are correct, give them a card with that number. Then give out a third card to each pair. Each pair must total up their card numbers. Does any pair have the number you have written on the board? If they do, they get a cube. Repeat several times

ACTIVITY 2
3 children

- *Adding three numbers (the largest number first and then pairs that make 10)*

Two sets of number cards (0 to 9) (PCM 3), post-it notes
Spread out the cards face down on the table. Each child takes a card and puts it face up on the table. The children, individually, add up the cards in their heads and then compare their answers. They agree a total, write it on a post-it note and stick it across the three cards. Repeat.

ACTIVITY 3
3 children

- *Adding three numbers by combining three sets*
- *Matching numbers to sets*

A set of dominoes
Spread out the dominoes face up. The children choose three dominoes and make a triangle with them. They write down the number of spots on each domino. They add up the three numbers and write the answer. Suggest that they check their addition by counting all the spots. Repeat.

ACTIVITY 4
3 children

- *Adding coins*
- *Matching amounts of money to numbers*

Number cards (1 to 20) (PCMs 3, 4), coins (1p, 2p, 5p), a feely bag
Each child takes a coin. They work out how much they have altogether. They find a card to match the total and place the coins on the card. Repeat, taking three different coins.

ACTIVITY 5
2-3 children

- *Adding three numbers*
- *Reasoning about numbers and systematising the search*

Number cards (1 to 12) (PCMs 3, 4)
Lay out the cards face up. Ask the children to choose three cards which add up to 15. How many different sets of three cards can they find?

ACTIVITY 6
3 children

- *Adding three numbers (totalling up to 20)*

Infant game 11: 'Addition slides', a dice, counters, cubes
(See instructions on the card.)

 N21 **Odd and even**

ACTIVITY 1
Whole class, in pairs

- *Matching numerals to numbers*
- *Recognising even and odd numbers*

Card for labels ('odd', 'even'), interlocking cubes

Each pair writes a number on a piece of paper. Choose a card and read out *Even* or *Odd*. Any child with a number which fits that category can have a cube. Repeat the activity, giving criteria for the number they write, e.g. *Write a number which is less than ten.*

ACTIVITY 2
3 children

- *Matching numerals to numbers*
- *Recognising even and odd numbers*

Two sets of number cards (1 to 20) (PCMs 3, 4)

Spread out the cards face down on the table. The children take turns to play. They turn over two cards and decide whether each number is even or odd. If they are both even, or both odd, the child keeps the cards. If not, they are turned face down again. Repeat until there are no cards left. Who has the most cards?

ACTIVITY 3
3 children

- *Matching numbers to objects*
- *Beginning to recognise even and odd numbers*

A set of dominoes, a large number line (1 to 12) (odd and even numbers in different colours)

Spread out the dominoes face up. Ask the children to add up the spots on the dominoes and to sort them into those with an even and those with an odd total. Look at the number line for help. Which set has the most dominoes?

ACTIVITY 4
3 children

- *Matching coins to amounts*
- *Recognising even and odd numbers*

Coins (1p, 2p, 5p), card for labels ('odd', 'even')

The children take two or three coins and add them up. They decide whether the total is even or odd. They place the coins in a pile by the appropriate card, then take another two or three coins and repeat the process. They continue until all the coins have been taken.

ACTIVITY 5
2-3 children

- *Adding two or more numbers*
- *Recognising even and odd numbers*
- *Reasoning about numbers*

Two sets of number cards (1 to 10) (PCM 3)

The children work together using the cards to make addition pairs which give an even answer, then addition pairs which give an odd answer. Which has more (even – odd + odd = even, even + even = even, odd + even = odd)? Do they know why this is?

N22 **Number patterns**

ACTIVITY 1
Whole class, in pairs

- *Adding two or more numbers*
- *Recognising addition pairs (up to 10)*
- *Reasoning about numbers*

Dominoes, a large number line (1 to 20)
Each pair of children has two dominoes. They must add up all the spots. Point to the 1 on the number line. *Does anyone have a pair of dominoes with a total of one spot? Yes.* Those children show their dominoes. Draw them on the board. Point to the 2. *Does anyone have a pair with a total of two spots? Yes.* Continue until all the children's pairs have been drawn on the board.

ACTIVITY 2
3 children

- *Adding two or more numbers*
- *Recognising addition pairs (up to 10)*

A set of dominoes, number cards (1 to 12) (PCMs 3, 4)
Spread out the dominoes face down on the table. Each child takes turns to pick a domino. They add up the spots. *Who has the largest number?* That child must find the matching number card. *Who has the next largest number? Who has the smallest number?* They find the matching cards each time. The children look at the three cards and add them up. They work out the total. They should check their answer by counting all the spots on the dominoes.

ACTIVITY 3
3 children

- *Adding two or more numbers*
- *Recognising addition pairs (up to 10)*
- *Reasoning about numbers*

A set of dominoes
Spread out the dominoes face up. The children make domino walls so that each of the bottom pairs of numbers add up to the one above.

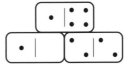 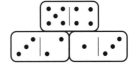

How many different walls can they make? Can they make a wall with the highest total possible? Can they make a wall with the lowest total possible?

ACTIVITY 4
3 children

- *Adding two numbers*
- *Recognising some addition pairs (up to 10)*

A set of dominoes, number cards (1 to 12) (PCMs 3, 4)
Lay out the dominoes face up. The children select all the dominoes with six spots on one half. They add the number of spots on each of these dominoes and match them to a card, then lay the cards in order. What do they notice? Repeat, asking the children to select all the dominoes with five spots on one half.

ACTIVITY 5
3 children

- *Recognising odd and even numbers*
- *Recognising patterns in numbers*

A set of dominoes (excluding the blanks)
Sort the dominoes into sets, 'even numbers of spots at both ends', 'odd numbers of spots at both ends' and 'odd number of spots at one end and even at the other'. Discuss what they notice.

N23 Ordering

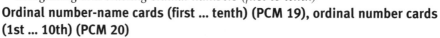

ACTIVITY 1
Whole class, in pairs

• *Recognising and ordering ordinal numbers (first to tenth)*
**Ordinal number-name cards (first … tenth) (PCM 19), ordinal number cards
(1st … 10th) (PCM 20)**
Shuffle one set of cards and spread them out, face up. The children put them in
order, from first to tenth. Collect the cards, reshuffle them and repeat, but from
tenth to first. Repeat with the other set of cards.

ACTIVITY 2
Pairs

• *Using ordinal numbers to state the position of objects in a line*
**Ordinal number-name cards (first … tenth) (PCM 19), ordinal number cards
(1st … 10th) (PCM 20), ten interlocking cubes (each a different colour)**
Place the ten cubes in a line. Shuffle one set of cards and place them in a pile,
face down. The children take turns to reveal a card and say the colour of the
cube in that matching position. The children check each other's answers.
Repeat with the other set of cards.

ACTIVITY 3
2-3 children

• *Recognising the ordinal number before and after a given ordinal number*
**Ordinal number-name cards (first … tenth) (PCM 19), ordinal number cards
(1st … 10th) (PCM 20)**
Shuffle one set of cards and place them in a pile, face down. The children take
turns to reveal a card, and say the position which comes after the one on the
card. The other children check. Ask them to repeat but this time saying the
position which comes before the one on the card. Repeat, using the other set of
cards.

ACTIVITY 4
3-4 children

• *Using ordinal numbers to state the position of objects in a line*
**Ordinal number-name cards (first … tenth) (PCM 19), ordinal number cards
(1st … 10th) (PCM 20)**
On the board, write the first ten letters of the alphabet. Shuffle one set of cards
and place them in a pile, face down. Taking turns, the children reveal the top
card in the pile. All the children write down the letter in the position stated on
the cards. Continue for all ten cards, so that each child has a string of ten
letters. The children check that each other's string of letters is the same. Repeat,
using the other set of cards and a new set of letters.

ACTIVITY 5
3-4 children

• *Using ordinal numbers to describe turns in a game*
• *Counting a set of objects by sorting them into tens and units*
A dice, interlocking cubes
The children play ten rounds. Each time the dice is thrown they must say
which throw it is, e.g. *The fourth throw is… one.* The children collect cubes to
match the throw of the dice. When they have enough cubes, they can make up
towers of ten. The winner is the player who has collected the most cubes after
ten rounds.

N24 # Ordering

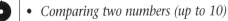

ACTIVITY 1
Whole class, then pairs

- *Comparing two numbers (up to 10)*
- *Recognising the larger and smaller*

Number cards (1 to 10) (PCM 3)

Each pair shuffles their cards and places them face down in a pile. The children take turns to reveal the top card from their pile. The child with the larger number keeps both cards. Continue for ten rounds. The winner is the player who collects the most cards. Repeat with the children collecting the smaller number cards. (For the whole class activity group the children in two teams, one set of cards for each team.)

ACTIVITY 2
3 children

- *Comparing three numbers (up to 10)*
- *Recognising 'larger', 'smaller' and 'between'*

Three sets of number cards (1 to 10) (PCM 3), counters

Each child shuffles a set of cards and places them face down in a pile. They take turns to reveal the top card from their pile. The child with the smallest number collects one counter, the largest collects two counters and the 'in between' collects three counters. If two children have the same number, they do not collect any counters. After ten rounds, the winner is the child with the most counters.

ACTIVITY 3
3 children

- *Recognising the set of numbers 'between' two others*

Two sets of number cards (1 to 10) (PCM 3), number track (1 to 10) (PCM 1), 1p coins

The children shuffle the two sets of cards and place them face down in two piles. Two of the children reveal the top cards in each pile while the third child is the 'between' player. He has to say all the numbers between the two numbers shown on the cards and collects one coin for each number. The children check that he is correct by placing a counter on each 'end' number on the number track. Repeat for three turns, then swap the 'between' player. Who collects the most money?

ACTIVITY 4
3 children

- *Locating different numbers lying between two given numbers*

Two sets of number cards (1 to 20) (PCMs 3, 4), number track (1 to 20) (PCM 1)

Place one set of cards face down in a pile, and spread out the other set, face up, on the table. Two of the children take a card from the pile. The third child is the 'between' player who collects the cards between these two numbers from those spread out on the table. They all check using the number track. Continue, taking turns to be the 'between' player, reshuffling the pile of cards if necessary. Return the 'between' cards.

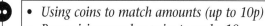 N25 Addition and money

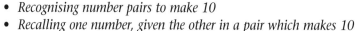

ACTIVITY 1
Whole class, in pairs

- *Using coins to match amounts (up to 10p)*
- *Recognising number pairs to make 10*
- *Recalling one number, given the other in a pair which makes 10*

Coins (1p, 2p, 5p), a feely bag, cubes

The children write down an amount between 1p and 10p on their paper. Take an amount between 1p and 10p out of the bag. Choose a child to work out how much you have, e.g. a 1p and a 5p makes 6p. Ask her to write the amount on the board. *How much more do you need to make 10p?* Any pair with the correct amount written on their page receives a cube. Repeat several times.

ACTIVITY 2
3 children

- *Using coins to make amounts up to 10p*
- *Giving change for 10p*

A collection of objects (labelled 1p, 2p, ... 8p), coins (1p, 2p, 5p, 10p)

One child is the shopkeeper, the others are shoppers. Each shopper takes one 10p and two 5p coins. The shopkeeper keeps the other coins. The shoppers take turns to buy something from the shop. The shopkeeper collects the money and gives change. Both the shoppers and shopkeeper check the change is correct. The children buy two items each. They return the items and the coins and the activity is repeated with a different shopkeeper.

ACTIVITY 3
4 children

- *Recognising number pairs to make 10*
- *Recalling one number, given the other in a pair which makes 10*

Two sets of number cards (0 to 10) (PCM 3), ten cubes (or counters)

Shuffle the cards and place them face down in a pile. They take turns to reveal a card and say the matching pair to make ten. The others use the counters to check. If they are correct they keep the card, if not they replace it at the bottom of the pile. Continue until all the cards are collected.

ACTIVITY 4
3 children

- *Matching numbers to objects*
- *Recognising number pairs to make 10*

Number cards (0 to 10) (PCM 3), beads, paper, crayons

Each child chooses a pair of cards which total ten, e.g. 4 and 6. They choose four beads in one colour and six beads in another colour. They make a pattern using these ten beads and copy the pattern onto paper, then write the matching addition, e.g. '4 + 6 = 10'. The children draw each other's patterns.

ACTIVITY 5
3-4 children

- *Recognising number pairs to make 20*

Number cards (10 to 20) (PCMs 3, 4), 2p coins

The cards are shuffled and placed in a pile face down. Taking turns, one child picks a card and has to say, immediately, what number pairs with it to make 20, e.g. they pick up 13 and must say *Seven*. If they are correct, they take a 2p coin. The children continue until one of them has 20p. Shuffle the cards and ask them to play again.

N26 Addition

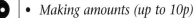

ACTIVITY 1
Whole class, in pairs

- *Making amounts (up to 10p)*
- *Reasoning about numbers*

Number cards (4 to 10) (PCM 3), coins (1p, 2p, 5p)
Each pair takes a number card and has to find at least three ways of adding to make that number using 1p, 2p and 5p coins. How many ways can they find? Give them ten minutes to work on this together. Choose a number, e.g. 7, and ask *Who has a way of making ... , e.g. 7p.* Write the options on the board, e.g. '1p + 2p + 2p + 2p' or '2p + 5p'. Then choose a different amount and repeat the process.

ACTIVITY 2
2 pairs

- *Recognising number pairs to make 7*

Interlocking cubes (two colours), squared paper
One pair of children builds a series of towers from one to seven cubes tall using only red cubes. The other pair does the same using only blue cubes. They put the towers together to make totals of eight, e.g. one red cube and seven blue cubes. The children order the new towers according to the number of red cubes at the bottom and record all the patterns on squared paper.

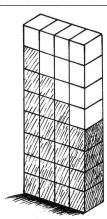

ACTIVITY 3
3 children

- *Recognising number pairs to make 6*
- *Recognising number pairs to make 7*

A set of dominoes
The children work together to find all the dominoes with a total of six spots and place them in order: (0/6), (1/5), (2/4) etc. They write down the number pairs. Next they find all the dominoes with a total of seven spots and place those in order. They continue for five spots etc., recording the number pairs each time.

ACTIVITY 4
3 children

- *Recognising number pairs to make 7*
- *Reasoning about numbers*

Two dice
The children investigate the different ways of throwing two dice to make a total of seven. They write them in order, then repeat for totals of six, then five etc.

ACTIVITY 5
3 children

- *Recognising number pairs to make 7*
- *Reasoning about numbers*

A dice, counters
The children examine the dice, looking carefully at the top and bottom numbers. They turn the dice slightly and look at the new top and bottom. What do they notice? (The top and bottom always make seven.) They take turns to throw the dice, count the spots and say how many spots there will be on the bottom side. They turn the dice over to check. If correct they collect a counter. They continue until one child has ten counters.

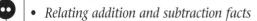

ACTIVITY 1
Whole class, in pairs

- *Relating addition and subtraction facts*
- *Recalling the number pairs (up to 10)*

Number cards (2 to 9) (PCM 3)
The children take two number cards. They use them to create an addition or subtraction which they write down. Encourage some pairs to use '–' and others to use '+'. Give the children five minutes to discuss the task and write their calculation. Ask, *Who has an answer of seven?* Any pair whose calculation has the answer 7 must write it on the board. Look at the different calculations and discuss them with the class. Repeat with different numbers, discussing different ways of making the same answer.

ACTIVITY 2
2 pairs

- *Relating addition and subtraction facts*
- *Recalling the number pairs (up to 10)*

Two sets of number cards (1 to 10) (PCM 3)
The children spread out the cards, face up. Each child takes a card and in their pairs they write an addition or subtraction for their cards, e.g. they take 5 and 8 and write '8 – 5 = 3'. They find the number card to match their answer, then swap their cards and paper with the other pair. They have to write a different addition or subtraction using those same three numbers, e.g. '3 + 5 = 8'. The children then compare their calculations. They replace the cards and repeat.

ACTIVITY 3
3-4 children

- *Relating addition and subtraction facts*
- *Recalling the number pairs (up to 10)*

Four sets of number cards (1 to 7) (PCM 3)
Shuffle the cards and spread them out face up on the table. In turn, each child takes three cards which they use to make an addition or subtraction, e.g. '3 + 1 = 4'. If the cards can be arranged to make a calculation, the child may keep those three cards. If not, they are replaced face up on the table. The children play until they have used all possible cards. Who has the most cards?

ACTIVITY 4
3 children

- *Adding two numbers by combining two sets*
- *Creating and reading additions*

Three sets of number cards (0 to 10) (PCM 3), card (for '+' and '=' cards), interlocking cubes
Each child builds a tower (up to ten) using cubes of two different colours. In turn, with the others' help, the children count up the cubes for each colour and match them to number cards. They find the card to match the total number of cubes as well and then arrange the cards to make additions or subtractions. They try to make three calculations, and read each one. Repeat, starting with different towers.

ACTIVITY 5
3 children

- *Relating addition and subtraction facts*
- *Recalling the number pairs (up to 10)*

Two sets of number cards (1 to 20) (PCMs 3, 4), card (for '+', '–' and '=' cards)
The cards are shuffled and placed in a pile, face down. Each child takes a card, then a second and then a third. They take cards until they have three which they can combine with the sign cards to form an addition or subtraction, e.g. 4 + 7 = 11. The others have to turn the cards around to make a different addition or subtraction e.g. 11 – 4 = 7. Repeat. How many different calculations have they made with all the cards?

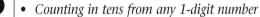

N28 Numbers to 100

ACTIVITY 1
Whole class, in pairs

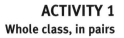

- *Counting in tens from any 1-digit number*
Number cards (1 to 9) (PCM 3), large number grid (1 to 100) (or PCM 18 – enlarged to A3), a plastic spider (or PCM 30)
Each pair takes a number card. Choose a number on the top row of the grid, e.g. 9. All the pairs with that number stand up and count in tens from that number, i.e. *Nine, nineteen, twenty-nine, thirty-nine…* Move the spider down the grid to help them. Choose another 1-digit number and repeat. Continue until every pair has counted.

ACTIVITY 2
3-4 children

- *Counting in multiples of ten*
Tens cards (10 to 100) (PCM 10)
Shuffle the cards and place them face down in a pile. The children take turns to pick up a card, e.g. 60, and count on in tens to 100, i.e. *Seventy, eighty, ninety, one hundred.* If they are correct, they keep the card, otherwise it is returned to the bottom of the pile. The children continue until all the cards have gone. Who has the most?

ACTIVITY 3
3-4 children

- *Counting in multiples of ten*
Tens cards (10 to 100) (PCM 10)
Shuffle the cards and place them face down in a pile. One child takes a card from the pile and says the number out loud, e.g. *Forty*. The other children take turns to count on in tens. *Fifty, sixty…* They continue until one child reaches *One hundred*. That child keeps the card and the counting stops. The children play again, with another child picking a card. They continue playing until all the cards have gone.

ACTIVITY 4
3 children

- *Matching numerals to multiples of ten*
- *Matching multiples of ten to sets of 10p coins*
Tens cards (10 to 100) (PCM 10), 10p coins
Each child takes a card and a matching number of coins. They carefully check each other's amounts. If they are correct, they keep the cards, otherwise the cards are returned to the bottom of the pile. Continue until all the cards have gone.

ACTIVITY 5
3 children

- *Counting in tens from any 1-digit number*
- *Matching numerals to numbers*
Number cards (1 to 100) (PCMs 3 to 9)
Working together, the children lay out the cards in lines which reflect 'spider counting'. E.g. they find 3, and then make a line which continues 13, 23, 33, 43… How many lines can they make?

ACTIVITY 1
Whole class, then 4 children

- *Recognising the number that is one more or less than a number (1 to 30)*
- *Recognising the number that is ten more or less than a number (1 to 30)*

Number cards (10 to 30) (PCMs 3 to 5), number grid (1 to 100) (PCM 18), counters

The children take turns to reveal a card and say the number which is ten more. They check each other's answers, using the number grid if necessary. If the children are correct, they keep the card. Let them continue until all the cards have gone. Who collects the most cards? Repeat with the children saying the numbers which are ten less, one more or, one less. (For the whole class activity use a large number grid and group the children in two teams.)

ACTIVITY 2
2-3 children

- *Recognising the number that is one more or less than a number (10 to 100)*
- *Recognising the number that is ten more or less than a number (10 to 100)*

Number grid (1 to 100) (PCM 18), counters, interlocking cubes

Ask the children to place a counter on 20 different numbers on the grid. The children take turns to point at a counter and another child in the group has to say what the hidden number is, then a number which is one more. If he is correct, he collects a cube, and removes the counter. The children continue until all the counters have been removed. Who has the most cubes? Extend the activity to saying numbers which are ten less, one more or, one less.

ACTIVITY 3
3 children

- *Recognising the number that is 10 more or less than a 2-digit multiple of 10*

Tens cards (10 to 100) (PCM 10), coins (10p, 1p)

Shuffle the cards and put them in a pile, face down. Each child takes a card, says the number which is ten less, then collects a matching amount of money. For example, a child picks the 40, says *Thirty*, and collects 30p. The children look at their amounts and the one who has the middle amount of money keeps it, while the others return theirs. Repeat three times. Who collects the most money? Who has the least? The winner is the child whose total is between the other two.

ACTIVITY 4
3 children

- *Recognising the number that is 10p more or less than an amount between 10p and 50p*
- *Combining two amounts of money (up to 50p)*

Number cards (10 to 50) (PCMs 3 to 6), coins (1p, 10p)

Shuffle the cards and put them in a pile, face down. Each child takes one card and collects a matching amount of money, e.g. if they take 27, they collect 27p. The children check each other's money to see if it matches the card. Repeat once more, then each player combines their two amounts of money. Suggest they change ten 1p coins for a 10p coin, if possible. Who has the most money? Who has the least? Who is between the two? Return the money and play several times more.

N30 Addition/subtraction

ACTIVITY 1
Whole class, in pairs

- *Adding ten to a 1-digit number (without counting in ones)*

Number grid (1 to 20) (PCM 1), large number cards (1 to 10), interlocking cubes

Deal each pair a number card. Shuffle the large number cards and place them in a pile, face down, then take one and read it out. The children add ten to that number. Choose a child to write the answer on the board. Use the grid to reinforce how to reach the total. Remind them that they do not have to count on in ones. Any pair with a card with that answer can take a cube. Place the card on the bottom of the pile and repeat.

ACTIVITY 2
4 children

- *Counting in tens from a 1-digit number*
- *Adding ten by counting on ten*

Number cards (1 to 9) (PCM 3)

Shuffle the cards and place them face down in a pile. One child takes a card from the pile and reads the number out loud, e.g. *Four*. The next child adds ten and says the answer, i.e. *Fourteen*. The children take turns to add ten and say the answer until one child says *Ninety-four*. That child takes the card and the counting stops. The children continue taking turns to select a card and say the first number. Each time, the child saying the final number keeps the card. They continue until all the cards have been used.

ACTIVITY 3
3 children

- *To add 9 to a 1-digit number*

Number cards (1 to 10) (PCM 3), number grid (1 to 20) (PCM 1), counters

Shuffle the cards and place them face down in a pile. The children take turns to select a card, add 9 (using the grid to help) and say the answer. The others check. If correct, the first child collects a counter. Repeat, swapping roles.

ACTIVITY 4
3 children

- *Counting in tens from a 1-digit number*
- *Adding ten by counting on ten*
- *Adding 10p to amounts of money*

Number cards (1 to 100) (PCMs 3 to 9), coins (1p, 10p)

One child takes a card in the twenties, e.g. 24, and places it in the middle of the table. The other children, between them, collect a matching amount in coins, i.e. two 10p and four 1p coins. The second child adds 10p, and the others find the matching card. The third child adds 10p and the others find the matching card. They continue until they have a line of cards and coins up to 94. Repeat with different starting numbers, always in the twenties.

ACTIVITY 5
3 children

- *Matching multiples of ten to sets of 10p coins*

Tens cards (10 to 100) (PCM 10), 10p coins

Shuffle the cards and place them in a pile face down. Each child takes a card in turn. They show the others and then match the number to the appropriate number of 10p coins. The children check each other's. Repeat several times.

ACTIVITY 6
2 children

- *Subtracting ten from a teen number (10 to 20)*

Number cards (10 to 20) (PCMs 3, 4), number grid (1 to 20) (PCM 1)

Spread the cards out face down. Take turns to reveal a card and subtract 10 from the number. Use the number grid to check. If correct, keep the card. If not, replace it face down. Continue until all cards have been removed. Who has collected the most?

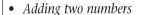

ACTIVITY 1
Whole class, in pairs

- *Adding two numbers*
- *Recognising addition pairs (up to 6)*

Three sets of number cards (0 to 5) (PCM 3)

Each pair writes down a number (between 5 and 10, inclusive). Shuffle the number cards and place them in a pile face down. Take two cards and read them out. *How much do they make in total?* Choose a child to write the answer on the board. Any pair which has the number written on their paper takes a cube. Place the cards on the bottom of the pile and continue in the same way. Who has the most cubes at the end? (You may need to let the children change their number half way through.)

ACTIVITY 2
4 children

- *Recognising the addition pairs to make ten*

Number track (1 to 10) (PCM 1), interlocking cubes, counters, a coin

The children place their counters at the start of the track. They take turns to toss the coin and move their counter. If it lands 'heads', they move one space along the track; 'tails' they move two spaces. The child looks at the number he has landed on. He must say the number which adds to that number to make ten, e.g. he lands on 4 and says *Six*. If he is correct, he takes a cube. When a child reaches the end of the track they start again at the beginning. Continue until someone has ten cubes.

ACTIVITY 3
4 children

- *Recognising the addition pairs to make ten*

Playing cards (Ace to 9)

Shuffle the cards and deal out four to each player. Place the remainder of the cards in a pile face down. Each child collects pairs of cards which make ten, e.g. 4 and 6 or 2 and 8. They place any pair face up in front of them. They take turns to choose a child and ask for a specific card number, e.g. *Amit, have you got a six?* He hands it over or the child asking takes the top card from the pile. The next player has a turn. The children continue until all the cards have gone. Who has the most pairs?

ACTIVITY 4
3 children

- *Recognising the addition pairs (up to 10)*

Number cards (0 to 9) (PCM 3), interlocking cubes (two colours)

Choose a target number between 6 and 10, e.g. 8. The children take turns to select a card. If the number is less than the target number, they take cubes in one colour which are equal to the number on their card and make them up to the target number using cubes in the other colour. E.g. if the target number is 8 and the card number is 5, they take five blue cubes and three red cubes. If the card number is equal to or more than the target number, they place it in a separate pile and take another card. The children continue until they have used all the cards. Change the target number and repeat.

ACTIVITY 5
3 children

- *Recognising change from 10p*

Card for price labels (1p, 2p … 10p), coins (1p)

Shuffle the labels and spread them out face down. Take turns to reveal a label and say the change you will receive from 10p. If correct, take coins to match the change, otherwise return the label face down. Check the answers using ten 1p coins, removing coins to match the price. When all labels are removed, who has the most money?

N32 Addition and money

ACTIVITY 1
Whole class, in pairs

- *Adding multiples of ten*
- *Adding sets of 10p coins*
- *Recognising 100p as £1*

Coins (10p, £1), dice

Ask each pair to write an amount of money which is one of the 'tens' but less than 70, e.g. 30p. Throw a dice and take that number of 10p coins, e.g. you throw a four and take four 10p coins. The children add that number of 10p coins to the amount they have written down. If any pair reaches exactly 100, they shout *Bingo!* and the game starts again. If not, throw the dice again. If any pair's total exceeds 100, they must cross out their number and write a new amount.

ACTIVITY 2
3-4 children

- *Making amounts which are multiples of ten using different coins*
- *Adding multiples of ten*

Tens cards (10 to 100) (PCM 10), coins (10p, 20p, 50p, £1)

Shuffle the cards and place them in a pile face down. The children take turns to reveal a card. They decide which coins to take to match the number on the card. The others check that they are correct. They write the number and draw around the coins.

ACTIVITY 3
4 children

- *Recognising coins*
- *Matching coins to a written number*

Number grid (1 to 100) (PCM 18 – enlarged to A3), coins (1p, 2p, 5p, 10p, 20p, 50p), a feely bag

Place all the coins in the bag. The children take turns to take out a coin. Each child must say what their coin is and match it to the correct square on the grid. (It does not matter if there is already a coin in that box.) They continue until the bag is empty.

ACTIVITY 4
3 children

- *Adding money to make 20p*
- *Reasoning about numbers and systematising their work*

Coins (1p, 2p, 5p, 10p, 20p)

Ask the children to explore and write down the different ways they could give someone 20p. How many ways can they find? Which group has found the most variations?

N33 Addition

ACTIVITY 1
Whole class, in pairs

- *Doubling numbers (up to 10)*
- *Adding near doubles of numbers (up to 10)*

Large number cards (1 to 10) (PCM 3 – enlarged to A3)

Ask half the pairs of children to write three even numbers (between 2 and 20), e.g. 12, 16 and 20. Ask the other half to write three odd numbers (between 3 and 20), e.g. 5, 13, and 15. Shuffle the cards and place them in a pile face down. Take a card and read out the number, e.g. *Four*. Choose a child to write the double on the board. Any pair with the matching number written down can cross it out. Write the card number on the board. *What is the next number, after four?* Write the addition for the near double of the number, i.e. '4 + 5 = '. Remind the children of the double: *Four and four makes eight*. Write the answer to the addition on the board, '4 + 5 = 9'. Any pair with this number crosses it out. Continue by taking another card and playing again. The first pair to cross out all three numbers can shout *Bingo!*

ACTIVITY 2
2 pairs

- *Doubling numbers (up to 10)*
- *Adding near doubles of numbers (up to 10)*

Number cards (1 to 10) (PCM 3)

Shuffle the cards and spread them face up on the table. The children take turns to take a card. Each pair has to collect two consecutive numbers. They write them down and double the smaller one. They then work out the total of the two card numbers. E.g. they take 2 and 3, write '2 + 2 = 4', and then write '2 + 3 = 5'. The pairs show each other and check. Repeat. Extend the activity by doubling the larger numbers instead.

ACTIVITY 3
4 children

- *Doubling numbers (up to 10)*
- *Recognising coins (up to 10p)*

Two sets of number cards (1 to 20) (PCMs 3, 4), coins (1p, 2p, 5p, 10p), a feely bag

Spread out the cards face up on the table. The children take turns to pull a coin from the bag. Each child says what their coin is, and how much money they would have if they had two of the same coin. They find the card to match the double. E.g. they take a 5p, double it, say *10p* and match the 5p to the 10 card. They continue until all the coins in the bag are used.

ACTIVITY 4
3 children

- *Doubling numbers (up to 20)*

Number cards (10 to 20) (PCMs 3, 4), post-it notes, interlocking cubes

Shuffle the cards and place them in a pile face down. The children take turns to take a card. They double the number and the others check using cubes. They write the double on a post-it note and stick it on the card. They continue until all the cards have been doubled.

N34 Odd and even

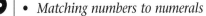

ACTIVITY 1
Whole class, in pairs

- *Matching numbers to numerals*
- *Recognising even and odd numbers*

Large number grid (1 to 100) (PCM 18 – enlarged to A3), number cards (1 to 100) (PCMs 3 to 9), card for labels ('even' and 'odd')

Give a card to each pair (Hint: choose an appropriate card for each pair). Choose a label, e.g. odd, and choose a row on the grid, e.g. 31 to 40. Identify the numbers on the row which match the label, e.g. 31, 33, 35, 37, 39. If any of the pairs have one of these numbers on their card they keep it and receive a new card. Continue, until one pair has three cards.

ACTIVITY 2
3-4 children

- *Counting in twos (up to 20)*
- *Matching numbers to objects*

Number cards (1 to 10) (PCM 3), interlocking cubes

Shuffle the cards and spread them out face up on the table. The children take turns to reveal a card. Each child has to count aloud in twos, holding up one finger for each number spoken, as many times as the number on their card. They take the same number of cubes as the number spoken and build a tower. E.g. they take the 3 card, say *Two, four, six*, and take six cubes, then match the tower to the card. They continue until all the cards have towers.

ACTIVITY 3
2-3 children

- *Counting in twos (up to 20)*
- *Matching numerals to numbers*

Number cards (1 to 20) (PCMs 3, 4), 2p coins

Spread out the cards face up on the table. The children count aloud in twos (from 2 to 20). They work together to arrange the number cards in a line to match the numbers they have counted. When all the cards are in order, they match each card to 2p coins to make up each amount.

ACTIVITY 4
3 children

- *Recognising even and odd numbers*
- *Understanding tens and units in 2-digit numbers*
- *Reasoning about numbers*

Number cards (0 to 9) (PCM 3)

Spread out the cards face up on the table. The children work together to make 2-digit numbers using the cards. However, the numbers must be even, no matter which way round the digits are written, e.g. 24 and 42. How many different even numbers can they make?

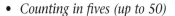

ACTIVITY 1
Whole class, in pairs

- *Counting in fives (up to 50)*
- *Matching numerals to multiples of five*

Number cards (1 to 10) (PCM 3)

Each pair draws three circles on their paper and writes a different 'five' number (between 5 and 50) in each circle, e.g. 10, 15 and 35. Shuffle the cards and place them in a pile face down. Take a card, read out the number and write it on the board. Encourage the class to count on in that number of fives, i.e. the card is 4 and you count *Five, ten, fifteen, twenty*, holding up one finger for each number. Write '20' on the board next to the '4'. Any pair with 20 written in one of their circles can cross it out. Take a new card and play again. The first pair to cross out all three numbers is the winner.

ACTIVITY 2
3-4 children

- *Counting in fives (up to 50)*
- *Matching multiples of five to sets of five objects*

Number cards (1 to 10) (PCM 3), interlocking cubes (in towers of five)

Shuffle the cards and spread them out face up on the table. The children take turns to reveal a card. Each child has to count aloud in fives, holding up one finger for each number spoken, until they are holding up the same number of fingers as the number on their card. They take that number of cubes and build a tower. E.g. they take the 3 card, they count *Five, ten, fifteen*, and take 15 cubes, then match the tower to the card. They continue until all the cards have towers.

ACTIVITY 3
2-3 children

- *Counting in fives (up to 50)*
- *Matching numerals to multiples of five*
- *Matching multiples of five to sets of 5p coins*

Number cards (5, 10, 15, 20 ... 50) (PCMs 10, 11), 5p coins

Spread out the cards face up on the table. The children count aloud in fives (from 5 to 50). They work together to arrange the number cards in order in a line to match the numbers they have counted. When all the cards are in a line, they place coins on each card to match the amount.

ACTIVITY 4
3 children

- *Counting in fives (up to 50)*
- *Matching numerals to multiples of five*
- *Understanding tens and units in 2-digit numbers*
- *Reasoning about numbers*

Number cards (0 to 9) (PCM 3)

Spread out the cards face up on the table. The children work together to make multiples of five using the cards. Discuss how we know whether a number is a 'five'. How many different multiples of five can they make?

ACTIVITY 5
3-4 children

- *Counting in threes to 30*

Number grid (1 to 100) (PCM 18), counters

The children put a counter on the number 3 on the grid. They continue putting counters on every third square, counting in threes, i.e. 3, 6, 9 ... The children remove the counters one by one and write the numbers as they do so.

N36 Ordering

ACTIVITY 1
Whole class, then 3-4 children

• *Ordering a set of numbers (in the range 1 to 20)*
Number cards (1 to 20) (PCMs 3, 4), number track (1 to 20) (PCM 1), counters
Deal three cards to each child. The children place them in a line, in order from smallest to largest. They check each other's line using the number track to check. Ask the children to replace the cards, reshuffle and repeat the exercise. Extend the activity by dealing out four and then five cards. (For the whole class activity demonstrate using large number cards, with the children pegging them in order on a line.)

ACTIVITY 2
3 children

• *Ordering a set of numbers (in the range 1 to 20)*
Number cards (1 to 20) (PCMs 3, 4)
The children take turns to deal at random, face up, a line of five cards. They swap the position of two of the cards and continue swapping pairs, until all the cards are in order from smallest to largest. The children should count how many swaps it takes to put all the cards in order and make a note of it. After one turn each, declare that the player who had the fewest swaps is the winner. Let the children play several times. Extend the activity by using cards beyond 20.

ACTIVITY 3
3-4 children

• *Recognising all the numbers which lie between two numbers (in the range 1 to 20)*
Number cards (1 to 20) (PCMs 3, 4), number track (1 to 20) (PCM 1), interlocking cubes
The children choose two cards, and spread the rest out face up. They take turns to find a card which lies between the two chosen ones. Allow them to use the number track to check. The first player unable to find a card loses. The others collect a cube each. The children reshuffle the cards and play the game several times. Who collects the most cubes?

ACTIVITY 4
3 children

• *Recognising ordinal numbers (up to tenth)*
Ordinal number-name cards (first … tenth) (PCM 19), ten interlocking cubes (ten different colours)
Shuffle the number-name cards and lay them out, face down. The children place ten cubes in a line and decide which cube is first in the line and which is last. The children take turns to reveal a card, e.g. fifth, and say the colour of the cube in this position. The other children check they are correct. When all the cards have been used, the children reshuffle them and repeat the activity several times.

ACTIVITY 5
3 children

• *Recognising ordinal numbers (up to twentieth)*
Number cards (1 to 20) (PCMs 3, 4), 20 interlocking cubes (of different colours)
Shuffle the cards and place them face down in a pile. The children place the cubes in a line. They take turns to reveal a card, e.g. 14 and say its position, e.g. cube fourteenth. They count along the line and say which colour cube is in that position, using the correct language, e.g. *The fourteenth cube is yellow.*

ACTIVITY 1
Whole class, in pairs

- *Recalling number pairs to make 10*
- *Adding three numbers by bridging through ten*

Number cards (0 to 9) (PCM 3), a dice

Each pair draws three circles on their paper and writes a different 'teen' number in each circle, e.g. 11, 15 and 17. Shuffle the cards and place them in a pile face down. Take a card, read out the number and write it on the board, e.g. 4. *What do we need to add to this number to make ten?* Write the answer on the board with a plus sign next to the card number, i.e. 4 + 6. Choose a child to throw the dice, e.g. three. Write that number on the board as part of the addition, followed by the equals sign '4 + 6 + 3 ='. Encourage the children to add the last number to the 'hidden' ten. Choose a child to write the total on the board. Read the addition '4 + 6 + 3 = 13'. If any pair has this number in one of their circles, they can cross it out. Take another card and play again. The first pair to cross out all their numbers shouts *Bingo!*

ACTIVITY 2
3 children

- *Recalling number pairs to make 10*
- *Adding two numbers by bridging through 10*

Three sets of number cards (1 to 9) (PCM 3)

Write '11' on a sheet of paper, this is the target number. Shuffle one set of cards and place them in a pile face down. Spread out the other two sets face up on the table. One child takes a card from the pile e.g. 6 and places it next to the target. Another child looks at the face up cards and finds the number, e.g. 4, which adds to the card number to make ten. He places that card next to the target as well. The third child then replaces one of the two chosen cards with its 'next' number to make '11', e.g. they could replace 4 with 5, or 6 with 7, etc. The children add up the numbers on the cards. They should total 11, e.g. '6 + 5 = 11'. Repeat, starting with another card.

ACTIVITY 3
3 children

- *Recognising coins (up to 10p)*
- *Adding three coins*

Coins (1p, 2p, 5p), interlocking cubes

Spread out the coins on the table. The children take a coin each. They work together to find out how much they have in total. Suggest that they match the coins to cubes to help them, e.g. two cubes for 2p. When they have agreed how much they have, they draw around the three coins and write the total. They repeat the activity, starting with a different coin each.

ACTIVITY 4
3 children

- *Recalling number pairs to make 10*
- *Using known facts to add two numbers*

Two sets of number cards (0 to 10) (PCM 3)

Spread out the cards face up on the table. The children work together to find pairs of cards which total 11. When they have made all the pairs, they can write them in a list, e.g. '1 + 10', '2 + 9...' Repeat with pairs which make 12. One card is missing. Which is it?

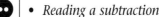 Subtraction

ACTIVITY 1
Whole class, in pairs

- *Reading a subtraction*
- *Subtracting using knowledge of place-value*

Number cards (11 to 19) (PCM 4)

Each pair of children draws three circles on their paper and then writes a different number (between 1 and 9, inclusive) in each circle, e.g. 1, 5 and 7. Shuffle the cards and place them in a pile face down. Take a card, read out the number and write it on the board, e.g. '14'. *What number would we need to take away from fourteen to leave ten?* Write the correct subtraction, i.e. '14 – 4'. Choose a child to write the answer '10' on the board. Read the subtraction, '14 – 4 = 10'. If any pair has written down the number that was subtracted, they can cross it out. Take another card and play again. The first pair to cross out all their numbers shouts *Bingo!*

ACTIVITY 2
3 children

- *Subtracting by taking away*
- *Subtracting using knowledge of place-value*

Number cards (1 to 20) (PCMs 3, 4), card for labels ('–', '='), a calculator, interlocking cubes

The children take turns to make a subtraction using the cards, e.g. '16 – 4 = 12'. The others check that it is correct using the calculator. They are rewarded with a cube, and the cards are replaced. The children continue, swapping roles until everyone has at least three cubes.

ACTIVITY 3
4 children

- *Subtracting objects by taking away*
- *Subtracting using knowledge of place-value*

Number cards (10 to 20) (PCMs 3, 4), a dice, interlocking cubes

Shuffle the cards and place them face down in a pile. The children take turns to reveal a card and throw the dice. They subtract the dice number from the card number and collect cubes to match the answer. The winner is the first player to collect 20 cubes.

ACTIVITY 4
2-3 children

- *Subtracting by taking away, or counting back one or two*

Number grid 3 (PCM 15), blank number grid (PCM 16)

Working together, the children take away two from every number on the grid. They write the answers in the matching spaces on the blank grid.

ACTIVITY 5
3 children

- *Subtracting using a knowledge of place-value*
- *Reasoning about numbers*

Number cards (10 to 39) (PCMs 3 to 6), number grid (0 to 39) (PCM 17), interlocking cubes

Shuffle the cards and place them in a pile face down. One child takes a card and shows the others. He chooses a number from the grid without telling the others. He subtracts that number from the card number and says the answer out loud. The others have to guess which number was chosen from the grid. If they are correct they take a cube each. The next child takes a card and repeats the process.

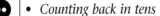

ACTIVITY 1
Whole class, in pairs

- *Counting back in tens*
- *Subtracting ten from a 'teen' number*

Number cards (1 to 10) (PCM 3), two sets of number cards (11 to 20)
(PCMs 3, 4), number grid (PCM 1), interlocking cubes

Each pair has a number card (between 1 and 10). Shuffle the other number cards and place them in a pile face down. Take one of the cards and read it out. The class must take ten from that number. Choose a child to write the answer on the board. Use the grid to check. Remind the class that it is not necessary to count back in ones. Any pair with the answer on their card can take a cube. Place the card on the bottom of the pile and repeat.

ACTIVITY 2
3 children

- *Counting back in tens from a 2-digit number*
- *Matching the numeral to a 2-digit number*

Number cards (1 to 100) (PCMs 3 to 9), a book (with about 100 pages), number grid (1 to 100) (PCM 18)

The children take turns to open the book towards the end and say the page number out loud, e.g. *Ninety-one*. They count back in tens to reach a number less than ten. The others keep a check using the number grid. Were they correct? If so, they take the card which matches the page number. The children continue taking turns until they have collected three cards each.

ACTIVITY 3
4 children

- *Counting back in tens from a 2-digit number*
- *Matching the numeral to a 2-digit number*

Number cards (80 to 100) (PCMs 8, 9), counters

One child chooses a card, e.g. 86, writes the number down and passes the paper to the next child, who writes the number which is ten less, i.e. 76. The children continue passing the paper round and writing ten less each time. If a child writes a number with two matching digits (66, 44, etc), they collect a counter. When the children reach a number less than ten, they stop. The children play again, taking turns to start, until one player has three counters.

ACTIVITY 4
2-3 children

- *Counting back in tens from a large 2-digit number*
- *Matching the numeral to a 2-digit number*

Number cards (91 to 99) (PCM 9), interlocking cubes, number grid (1 to 100) (PCM 18)

Shuffle the cards and place them face down in a pile. The children take turns to reveal the top card, e.g. 96, and count back in tens round the group *Ninety-six, eighty-six, seventy-six … six*, using the number grid to help, if necessary. The child to say the last 1-digit number collects a cube. Continue until all the cards have been used.

ACTIVITY 5
3 children

- *Counting back in tens from a 2-digit number*
- *Subtracting multiples of ten from a 2-digit number*
- *Reasoning about numbers*

Number grid (1 to 100) (PCM 18), a dice, interlocking cubes

One child chooses a number from the grid (between 60 and 100) without telling the others, e.g. 66. He throws the dice and subtracts that number of tens from his chosen number and says the answer out loud, e.g. he throws 6, takes off 60 and calls out *Six*. The others have to guess which number was chosen from the grid. If they are correct they can take a cube each. The next child chooses a grid number (between 60 and 100) and repeats the process.

N40 # Addition and money

ACTIVITY 1
Whole class, in pairs

- *Making amounts of money using coins (1p to 50p)*
- *Recognising coins and their values*

Write different amounts of money (up to 50p) on pieces of paper and give one to each pair. Draw and write the value of all the coins on the board. Ask the children to write down several ways to make their amount of money using coins. Discuss their different ways. Repeat.

ACTIVITY 2
3 children

- *Making amounts of money using coins (1p to 50p)*
- *Recognising coins and their values*

Fives cards (5, 10, 15, 20 .... 100) (PCMs 10, 11), coins (5p, 10p, 20p, 50p)

Shuffle the cards and place them in a pile face down. The children take turns to take a card and place it face up on the table. Working together, they decide how to match that amount of money using coins. When they have decided, they leave the coins on the card.

ACTIVITY 3
3 children

- *Making amounts of money which are multiples of ten, using coins*
- *Recognising coins*

Tens cards (10, 20, 30 ... 100) (PCM 10), coins (5p, 10p), counters

Shuffle the cards and place them face up on the table. Ask the children to match each one with the appropriate amount of coins. There must be at least two coins on each card.

ACTIVITY 4
3 children

- *Making amounts of money using coins (1p to 50p)*
- *Recognising coins and their values*

Number grid (1 to 100) (PCM 18), coins (1p, 2p, 5p, 10p, 20p, 50p), interlocking cubes

One child chooses a number from the grid without telling the others which one he has chosen. He then matches this number to the correct amount of coins. The others have to say which number was chosen. If they are correct they can each take a cube. The next child then chooses a grid number and repeats the process.

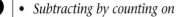

ACTIVITY 1
Whole class, in pairs

- *Subtracting by counting on*
- *Using addition and subtraction facts to solve money problems*

Number cards (10 to 20) (PCMs 3, 4)

Each pair writes down three amounts of money (between 1p and 10p inclusive). Shuffle the cards and take one. Hold it up and write the matching amount of money on the board. *I have saved this amount*, e.g. '14p'. *How much more do I need to make twenty pence?* Write '+ ? = 20p'. Give the pairs a few minutes to decide, e.g. 6p. Any pair which has that amount written down may cross it out. Continue playing until one pair has all three numbers crossed out.

ACTIVITY 2
4 children

- *Subtracting by counting on*
- *Using addition and subtraction facts to solve money problems*

Coins (1p to 20p), card for labels ('1p' to '10p')

One child writes down an amount (between 1p and 20p) e.g. '16p'. The next child takes coins to make that amount, e.g. 10p, 5p and 1p. The others check. The third child says how much more is needed to make 20p and takes a card label to match, e.g. 4p. The fourth child takes that amount in coins. The children put the two sets of coins together and check that they make 20p in total. They repeat, taking different roles.

ACTIVITY 3
3-4 children

- *Subtracting by counting on*
- *Using addition and subtraction facts to solve money problems*
- *Reasoning about numbers*

Coins (1p to 50p), number cards (10 to 90) (PCMs 3 to 9), card for labels ('10p', '20p' ... to '90p')

Shuffle the cards and place them face down in a pile. One child takes a number card, e.g. 54. The next child takes coins to make that amount, e.g. 50p, 2p and 2p. The other children decide which which label is the **next** multiple of ten above the amount they have, e.g. 60p. Together they decide how much more they need to make that amount, e.g. 6p. They take that amount in coins, and place the two cards and the 6p together. They repeat, taking different roles.

ACTIVITY 4
2-3 children

- *Matching amounts to coins*
- *Recognising coins*

Coins (1p to 20p), card for labels ('1p' to '20p')

One child takes a label and reads it aloud. The other two children match the label with the appropriate coins. E.g. the first child takes the label '8p', and the others match it with a 5p coin and three 1p coins. They repeat, swapping roles.

M1 Length

ACTIVITY 1
Whole class, then individually

- *Indirectly comparing the heights of children*
Large sheets of paper, a marker pen, Blu-tack
Stick the sheets of paper on the wall one above the other so they can be used to record the height of the children. Draw a vertical line down the paper. The children take turns to stand against the paper. Mark their height against the vertical line and write their name alongside it. When all the children have been measured, compare the heights of different pairs of children. Who is tallest? Who is shortest? The children draw themselves, then a taller and a shorter person.

ACTIVITY 2
3-4 children

- *Directly comparing the lengths of pairs of objects*
A collection of objects of different lengths
The children choose a pair of objects and compare their length. Make sure that they align them at one end to achieve a clear comparison. They draw the two objects, side by side, labelling them 'longer' and 'shorter'? Repeat, drawing at least three pairs of objects.

ACTIVITY 3
3-4 children

- *Directly comparing the heights of pairs of objects*
A collection of tall objects
The children choose a pair of objects and compare their height by standing them next to each other on the table or the floor. They draw the two objects, side by side, labelling them 'taller' and 'shorter'. Repeat, drawing at least three pairs of objects.

ACTIVITY 4
3-4 children

- *Directly comparing the length of one object with a set of other objects*
A collection of objects of different lengths
The children choose one object. They sort the other objects into two groups – those which are longer and those which are shorter than their chosen object. Repeat with different objects.

ACTIVITY 5
3+ children

- *Indirectly comparing the length of an object with a set of other objects*
- *Identifying objects of equal length*
A collection of objects of varying length, strips of paper or card
The children each cut a strip of paper or card to match the exact length of a chosen object. They use this strip to compare the length of the chosen object with the lengths of other objects. They make a list of 'longer' and 'shorter' objects, drawing pictures of the objects in each category. Can they find some objects which are almost equal in length to their chosen object?

M2 Length

ACTIVITY 1
Whole class, then 3-4 children

• *Directly comparing the length of one object with a set of other objects*
A collection of objects of varying length, straws
The children sort the objects into those which are longer than one straw, and those which are shorter than one straw. They place two straws end to end, and re-sort the objects into those which are longer than and those which are shorter than two straws. Extend the activity by using three straws.

ACTIVITY 2
3-4 children

• *Directly comparing the lengths of pairs of objects*
Dominoes, a selection of books (some about the length of six dominoes)
The children place six dominoes in a line. They find a book which is about the same length as their line. They carefully draw the book and the line of dominoes. Tell them to take care to draw all the dominoes as near as possible the same size.

ACTIVITY 3
Pairs

• *Directly comparing the heights of pairs of objects*
Strips of paper, scissors, 1p coins
The children cut strips of paper the same length as their hand span (the distance from the tip of the thumb to the tip of the little finger with the hand outstretched). They then label these with their name and decorate them with a pattern. The children measure the lengths of the strips using 1p coins. How much is each child's hand span worth?

ACTIVITY 4
3-4 children

• *Indirectly comparing the heights of children*
Non-standard measuring units (e.g. straws, pegs, new crayons)
The children choose a length based on the unit, e.g. six straws. They try to find objects which are about six straws long, draw the objects and label them. Repeat the process with a different length, e.g. ten straws.

ACTIVITY 5
3-4 children

• *Indirectly comparing the length of an object with a set of other objects*
• *Identifying objects of equal length*
A collection of objects of varying length, different non-standard measuring units (e.g. interlocking cubes, straws, dominoes)
The children choose an object and measure its length using towers of ten interlocking cubes. They must estimate the length before measuring. Ask them to draw the object and record the length in towers. They repeat the exercise using the other units as measures. Repeat, measuring different objects.

M3 Time

ACTIVITY 1
Whole class, then pairs

• *Showing the hour time on an analogue clock*
An analogue clock with moveable hands, number cards (1 to 12) (PCMs 3, 4)
The cards are shuffled and put in a pile face down. One pair chooses a card from the pile, e.g. 2. The other pair sets the hands of the clock to show that time, i.e. two o'clock. The children continue taking turns until all the cards have been used.

ACTIVITY 2
3-4 children

• *Showing and ordering the hour times on an analogue clock*
Clock-face sheet (PCM 22), scissors
The children draw hands on the clocks to show different 'o'clock' times. They cut them out and order them.

ACTIVITY 3
3-4 children

• *Recognising key times of the day*
• *Reading the hour time on an analogue clock*
Paper, crayons or paints
The children draw or paint pictures showing the activities they do at each hour of the day. Display their pictures on the wall under drawings of appropriate clock faces.

ACTIVITY 4
3-4 children

• *Showing and ordering the hour times on an analogue clock*
Clock-face sheet (PCM 22), number cards (1 to 12) (PCMs 3, 4), pencils, scissors, a large sheet of paper, glue
The cards are shuffled and placed face down in a pile. The children take turns to reveal a card. They draw hands on a clock face to show the hour, e.g. four o'clock. They carry on until all the clocks on the sheet show a different time, then cut out the clocks and display them, in order, on a larger sheet of paper.

ACTIVITY 5
3-4 children

• *Writing the o'clock times*
• *Recognising events that occur at each hour of the day (in order)*
Clock-face sheet (PCM 22), scissors, glue, a large sheet of paper
The children make a time line of the day. They write the hours on the clock faces (from 7 o'clock to 6 o'clock). They cut out the clocks and stick them onto paper in order. Ask them to write or draw, under each clock, something that they do at that time of the day.

M4 Time

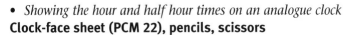

ACTIVITY 1
Whole class, then 3-4 children

- *Showing the half hour time on an analogue clock*
- *Associating half past times with events in the day*

An analogue clock with moveable hands

Without showing the rest of the group, one child sets the clock to show half past an hour, e.g. half past eight. He describes what he might be doing at that time of day, e.g. he might say *I would be going to bed*. The other children have to guess the time on the clock. The child who guesses correctly sets a new time.

ACTIVITY 2
3-4 children

- *Showing the hour and half hour times on an analogue clock*

Clock-face sheet (PCM 22), pencils, scissors

The children draw hands on the clocks to show different 'o'clock' and 'half past' times. These can be cut out and put in the correct order.

ACTIVITY 3
2 pairs

- *Showing and reading the hour and half hour times on analogue clocks*

An analogue clock with moveable hands, clock-face sheet (PCM 22)

One pair sets a half past time on the clock face and says the time. The other pair must draw in the hands on one of the clocks on the clock-face sheet. Check that the clocks match, then reverse the roles. Continue until all the clock faces have been filled in.

ACTIVITY 4
5-6 children

- *Showing and reading the hour and half hour times on analogue clocks*

Number cards (1 to 12) (PCMs 3, 4), an analogue clock face with moveable hands, clock-face sheet (PCM 22), interlocking cubes

Shuffle the cards and place them face down in a pile. *Let's play Clock Bingo.* All the children except one, who is the caller, fill in four different half past times on their clock face sheet. The caller takes the top card from the pile, reads the number and sets the clock to show half past that hour, e.g. if the card is 5, the child sets the clock to half past five. If one of the children has drawn in the matching time, he covers it with a cube. The caller continues turning over cards and setting the clock. The winner is the first player to cover all four of their clock faces. Repeat the game with a different child as the caller.

M5 # Weight

ACTIVITY 1
Whole class, then 2-3 children

- *Comparing the weight of two objects*
- *Finding objects which are lighter than a given object*
- *Recognising that weight and size are not necessarily related*

An object to weigh (e.g. a book), a balance
Encourage the children to find things which are lighter than the book. How many things can they find? Are some of them larger than the book?

ACTIVITY 2
2-3 children

- *Comparing the weights of two objects*
- *Recognising that weight and size are not necessarily related*

A small object (e.g. a paintbrush), a balance
How many small things can the children find which are heavier than the paintbrush? They should look for things the same size or smaller.

ACTIVITY 3
3-4 children

- *Estimating the ordering of objects by weight*
- *Comparing the weights of several objects*

Three objects (e.g. a shoe, a book and a pencil case), a balance
Which object is the heaviest? Which is the lightest? Let the children feel them and talk about how they are going to find out. They check their estimates using a balance. When they have established the order, they draw them in that order, from lightest to heaviest.

ACTIVITY 4
3-4 children

- *Estimating the ordering of objects by weight*
- *Comparing the weights of several objects*

A balance
The children choose a classroom object (help them to make an appropriate choice). They estimate two objects that will be lighter, and two objects that will be heavier, than the object. They check their estimates using the balance, then order the objects from heaviest to lightest and record the order.

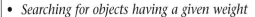 M6 Weight

ACTIVITY 1
Whole class, then 2-3 children

- *Searching for objects having a given weight*
- *Weighing objects using non-standard units*

A balance, wooden bricks

Place twenty bricks on one side of the balance. Can the children find some objects which weigh the same as twenty bricks? (For the whole class activity demonstrate using a different number of bricks.)

ACTIVITY 2
4 children

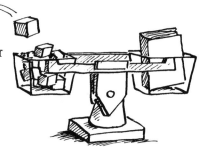

- *Estimating the weight of objects using non-standard units*
- *Weighing objects using non-standard units*

A balance, wooden bricks, a book

Each child estimates the number of bricks that will balance the book. Write down their estimates. The children check by weighing the book in bricks.

ACTIVITY 3
Pairs

- *Weighing objects using non-standard units*
- *Comparing the weights of two objects*

A balance, wooden bricks, children's shoes

The children work together to weigh their shoes in bricks. Make a chart which shows the number of bricks each person's shoe weighs.

ACTIVITY 4
3-4 children

- *Estimating the weight of objects using non-standard units*
- *Weighing objects using non-standard units*

A balance (bucket), ten objects, bean-bags (or bricks/interlocking cubes/cups of sand)

The children estimate the number of bean bags to balance each of five objects. They order the objects and record the estimated order. They check their estimates and record the new order, if necessary.

M7 **Time**

ACTIVITY 1
Whole class, then 3-4 children

- *Recognising the 'day after' a given day of the week*
- *Naming the days of the week*

Day cards (PCM 23), interlocking cubes

Shuffle the cards and place them face down in a pile. The children take turns to pick a card, e.g. Tuesday, and say what the next day is, i.e. *Wednesday*. If they are correct, they take a cube. They return the card to the bottom of the pile. The children continue taking turns until each player has three cubes. (For the whole class activity group the children in two teams.)

ACTIVITY 2
2-3 children

- *Ordering the days of the week*
- *Recognising that there are seven days in a week*
- *Beginning to recognise the first, second, third, ... days of the week*

Day cards (PCM 23), interlocking cubes

The children lay out the cards in order, from Sunday to Saturday. They place one cube on the first day of the week (Sunday), two cubes on the second, etc., reading the days as they do so. How many days are there?

ACTIVITY 3
3-4 children

- *Beginning to associate activities to given days of the week*
- *Beginning to recognise the concept of a weekly diary*

Crayons, day cards (PCM 23)

The children draw a picture of something they have done or will do on each day of the week, Monday to Saturday, and label each picture. Extend the activity by asking the children to draw a picture for Sunday.

ACTIVITY 4
3 children

- *Recognising the 'day before' and the 'day after' a given day of the week*

Day cards (PCM 23), interlocking cubes

Shuffle the cards and deal two to each player. Place the last card face up in the centre of the table. If the first child has the day before or the day after the card in the centre, he places it in the correct position. Otherwise he misses a turn and takes a cube. The second child must place the day before or day after one of the two cards in the centre. Otherwise he takes a cube. The children continue until all the cards are laid out. The winner is the player with the fewest cubes.

ACTIVITY 5
Pairs

- *Recognising the days of the week (in order)*

Concept keyboard with a word processor (create overlay and file to match)

The children work together to create the story of 'Worm'. They press the day and then the activity. Each day reads, 'On Monday', 'On Tuesday...' Each picture reads 'Worm went swimming' etc.

| Monday |
| Tuesday |
| Wednesday |
| Thursday |
| Friday |
| Saturday |
| Sunday |

M8 Capacity

ACTIVITY 1
Whole class, then 2-4 children

- *Using the vocabulary related to capacity*
A non-liquid filler (e.g. peas, lentils, sand) and a collection of containers (some partly filled, some half filled, some nearly filled, some full and some empty)
The children sort the containers and describe each in terms of empty, nearly empty, half full, nearly full, full. (For the whole class activity demonstrate pictorally or using a separate set of containers.)

ACTIVITY 2
2-4 children

- *Using the vocabulary related to capacity*
- *Filling containers to given capacities*
A non-liquid filler (e.g. peas, lentils, sand) and a collection of pairs of containers
The children pour the filler into each container so that it is half full. They continue pouring to make each container nearly full, and finally so that each is full.

ACTIVITY 3
3-4 children

- *Estimating the order of capacity of a set of containers*
- *Measuring capacity using non-standard units*
A collection of small containers, an eggcup, water
The children estimate which container will need the most eggcupfuls to fill it, and which the least, and place the containers in order of estimated capacity. They measure the capacity of each container by continually filling the eggcup and pouring it into the container until it is full, counting as they go. The children record the results and check the estimated order.

ACTIVITY 4
3-4 children

- *Estimating the order of capacity of a set of containers*
- *Measuring capacity using non-standard units*
A collection of containers, yoghurt pots, water
Repeat Activity 3 using a yoghurt pot as the measure. The children start by estimating the capacity of each container in terms of yoghurt pots.

ACTIVITY 5
3-4 children

- *Measuring the capacity of a container using different non-standard units*
- *Estimating capacity*
A large container (e.g. a jug), a collection of smaller non-standard measures (e.g. jam-jar, beaker, yoghurt pot, tin, eggcup)
The children measure the capacity of the jug using a different non-standard unit in turn. Before each measure the children estimate how many of the unit will be required, and write it down.

M9 Time

ACTIVITY 1
Whole class, then 4-5 children

- *Associating particular events with hour times of the day*

Number cards (1 to 12) (PCMs 3, 4), interlocking cubes

Shuffle the cards and place them face down in a pile. The children take turns to pick a card and do an action or a mime appropriate to that time of day. E.g. if they pick 7, they might do an imitation of someone waking up. If one of the other children guesses the correct time, he takes a cube. The children continue taking turns until someone has three cubes. (Hint: You may decide, initially, to focus on key times of the day.) The activity could be simplified by creating cards with a picture clue in addition to the number.

ACTIVITY 2
3 children

- *Showing the time which is one hour after and one hour before an o'clock time*

Two sets of number cards (1 to 12) (PCMs 3, 4), an analogue clock with moveable hands, interlocking cubes

Spread out the cards face up. One child sets the clock hands. The others find the cards to match the hour before that time and the hour after that time. If they are correct they take a cube each. The children continue taking turns to set the hands until each player has four cubes.

ACTIVITY 3
3-4 children

- *Associating particular events with hour times of the day*
- *Recording hour times*

Two hoops, card for labels ('day', 'night'), clock-face sheet (PCM 22), pencils or paints, scissors

On the clock-face sheet, the children draw the hands to show a time, e.g. three o'clock. They cut it out and place it in the correct hoop, one labelled 'day', the other 'night'. They say what they might be doing at that time. E.g. *at three o'clock I play on the swings*. The children draw or paint a picture to go with each clock face.

ACTIVITY 4
3-4 children

- *Creating a day diary based on each hour of the day*
- *Recognising events in the day in relation to before or after midday and midnight*

Clock-face sheet (PCM 22), scissors, glue, a large sheet of paper

The children make a time diary for midnight to midday. They draw hands on clock faces to show 1 o'clock, 2 o'clock, ... 12 o'clock, cut out the clocks and stick them in line on a large sheet of paper. They draw pictures underneath each clock to show what they will be doing at each time, e.g. the first six pictures are likely to show sleeping. Ask the children to repeat the activity but this time the clocks should show from midday to midnight.

M10 Time

ACTIVITY 1
Whole class, in pairs

• *Ordering the months of the year*
Month cards (PCMs 24, 25)
Put out the month cards randomly in a straight line. Taking turns and changing
one card at a time, the children have to put them in order, from January to
December, then say the months in sequence. Repeat the activity, this time
swapping any two months at a time. Tell them to count how many swaps are
needed to put them in order.

ACTIVITY 2
3-4 children

• *Recognising the months belonging to each season*
Month cards (PCMs 24, 25), card (for seasons labels)
Shuffle the month cards and place them face down on the table. The children
arrange the four season labels in a line. They take turns to pick a month card,
decide to which season it belongs, and place it underneath the appropriate
label. Continue like this through all the months. Reshuffle the cards and repeat
the activity.

ACTIVITY 3
4 children

• *Recognising the months belonging to each season*
Month cards (PCMs 24, 25), interlocking cubes
Shuffle the cards and place them face down in a pile. Each child chooses to be
one of the four seasons. Remind the children that each season is three months
long. The children take turns to pick a card. They may keep the card if that
month is in their season. Otherwise they return the card to the bottom of the
pile and take a cube. When all the cards have gone, the winner is the player
with the fewest cubes.

ACTIVITY 4
3-4 children

• *Matching months of the year to their position in the year*
**Number cards (1 to 12) (PCMs 3, 4), month cards (PCMs 24, 25), interlocking
cubes**
Shuffle the number cards and place them face down in a pile. Spread out the
month cards face up on the table. The children take turns to pick a number
card from the pile and take the appropriate month, e.g. if they pick card 4, they
take 'April'. If they are correct, they keep the cards. Otherwise they replace the
month card face up on the table, return the number card to the bottom of the
pile and take a cube. The children continue taking turns until all the cards have
gone. The winner is the player with the fewest cubes.

ACTIVITY 5
Pairs

• *Recognising the different seasons*
Concept keyboard with a word processor (create overlay and file to match)
In pairs, the children choose a season and then the appropriate weather or
festival (depending on the children). The season would read, 'In spring', 'In
autumn' … The picture would read 'flowers begin to grow again' etc.

autumn	
spring	
summer	
winter	

S1 # 2-d shape

ACTIVITY 1
Whole class, then 3-4 children

- *Recognising and naming squares, circles, triangles, rectangles*
- *Creating and describing repeating sequences of shapes*

Plastic 2-d shapes or sticky coloured 2-d shapes (squares, rectangles, triangles, circles), paper

The children make repeating patterns using two shapes, by placing them in a line, e.g. square, square, triangle, square, square ... They can either make the patterns on a table or by sticking them onto paper. Extend the activity to making three shape patterns, e.g. triangle, rectangle, circle, triangle, rectangle, circle. (For the whole class activity use large shapes cut from coloured sugar paper.)

ACTIVITY 2
2 children

- *Recognising and naming square, rectangular, circular and triangular faces on 3-d shapes*

A collection of 3-d shapes (e.g. cubes, cuboids, pyramids, prisms, cylinders, cones), two hoops, card for labels ('triangular face', 'not triangular face')

The children sort the shapes into two sets according to whether or not they have a triangular face. Repeat for square faces, circular faces and rectangular faces.

ACTIVITY 3
4 children

- *Recognising and naming squares, circles, triangles, rectangles*

Shape cards (PCM 26)

Shuffle the cards and deal them out (two players have four cards, and two have five cards). The children choose to collect one of squares, circles, rectangles or triangles. They take turns to swap a card with another player. They continue swapping one card at a time until one child has three of their chosen shape.

ACTIVITY 4
4 children

- *Recognising and naming squares, circles, triangles, rectangles,*

Shape cards (PCMs 26, 27), counters

Spread out the cards face down on the table. The children take turns to reveal a card. According to the shape, they take one counter for a circle, two for a square, three for a triangle or four for a rectangle. For any other shape they take no counters. The children continue until all of the cards have been revealed. The winner is the player who has collected the most counters.

ACTIVITY 5
2-3 children

- *Recognising and naming square, rectangular, circular and triangular faces on 3-d shapes*
- *Describing the faces of 3-d shapes*

A collection of 3-d shapes (e.g. cubes, cuboids, pyramids, prisms, cylinders, cones), a feely bag

The children place the shapes in the bag. They take turns to reveal a shape and then describe the shape of each face, e.g. *Two squares and four rectangles*. They check each other's descriptions. The children continue taking turns until all of the shapes have been described. Which shapes have the same descriptions?

ACTIVITY 1
Whole class, then 3-4 children

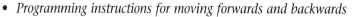
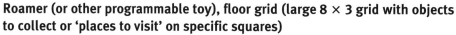

• *Programming instructions for moving forwards and backwards*
Roamer (or other programmable toy), floor grid (large 8 × 3 grid with objects to collect or 'places to visit' on specific squares)
The children follow instructions to collect a set of objects or visit places (e.g. park, home, school) on different grid squares. Extend the activity by asking children to write their own instructions.

ACTIVITY 2
3-4 children

• *Recognising forwards and backwards movements*
Infant game 9: 'Coin collector', a dice, counters
Each child places a counter at the start of the game. They take turns to throw the dice and move forwards the number of spaces. When they reach 20, they start to move backwards down the track. The winner is the first to return to the starting point.

ACTIVITY 3
3-4 children

• *Recognising forwards and backwards movements*
Number track (0 to 20) (PCM 1), a coin, a dice, counters
Each child places a counter on 10 on the number track (positioned vertically). They take turns to toss the coin (heads means forwards, tails means backwards) and roll the dice. They move their counter according to the toss of the coin and the roll of the dice, e.g. forwards, six. The winner is the first to move off the track.

ACTIVITY 4
2-3 children

• *Recognising left and right movements*
Number track (0 to 20) (PCM 1), playing cards (Ace to 6), counters
Each child places a counter on ten on the number track (positioned horizontally). Shuffle the cards and place them face down in a pile. The children take turns to reveal a card. If it is red, they move left; if it is black, they move right. They move their counter to match the direction and number of the card, e.g. left, four. If they come off the track, they score one point and go back to ten again. Who has scored the most points when all the cards are revealed?

ACTIVITY 5
3+ children

• *Following instructions for moving forwards and backwards along a line*
Number track (0 to 20) (PCM 1), two different coloured dice, counters, interlocking cubes
Ask the children to decide which dice will indicate 'forwards' moves and which will indicate 'backwards' moves. Each child places a counter on 10 on the number track (positioned vertically). They take turns to throw both dice, and move both forwards and backwards to match the numbers on the dice. As they land on the numbers on the track, they collect cubes to match the number they land on. They have five turns each. Who has collected the most cubes?

S3 3-d shape

ACTIVITY 1
Whole class, then 3-4 children

- *Recognising and naming cubes, cuboids, pyramids, spheres*

A collection of 3-d shapes (cubes, cuboids, pyramids, spheres), card for labels ('cube', 'cuboid', 'pyramid', 'sphere'), a feely bag

Spread out the labels face up on the table, and place the shapes in the bag. The children take turns to pick a shape from the bag and place it beside the correct label.

ACTIVITY 2
3+ children

- *Recognising and naming cubes, cuboids, pyramids, spheres, cylinders, cones*

A set of 3-d shapes (cubes, cuboids, pyramids, spheres, cylinders, cones), a book or board

Using the book or board as a 'wall', the children take turns to be in charge of the shapes, revealing them very slowly from behind the wall. The others have to name the shape as soon as they can. If they guess before it is fully revealed, they keep the shape, if not it goes to the child behind the 'wall'.

ACTIVITY 3
3-4 children

- *Recognising and naming cubes, cuboids, pyramids, spheres, cylinders, cones*

A collection of 3-d shapes (cubes, cuboids, pyramids, spheres, cylinders, cones), a feely bag

Place the shapes in the bag. The children take turns to feel for a shape and name it. They pull it out and if they are correct, they keep it. Otherwise, they replace it in the bag. The children continue until all of the shapes have been removed. Who has collected the most?

ACTIVITY 4
2+ children

- *Recognising and naming cuboids, pyramids, spheres*

Infant game 21: 'Shape Jump', a blank dice or cube (labelled as shown below), counters

(See instructions on the card.)

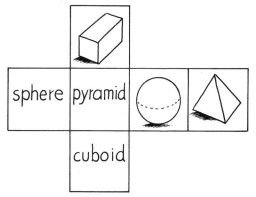

ACTIVITY 5
2+ children

- *Investigating the building of different cuboids using a fixed number of cubes*

Interlocking cubes

The children investigate ways of making different cuboids with twelve cubes.

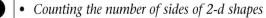

S4 2-d shape

ACTIVITY 1
Whole class, in groups of 3-4

- *Counting the number of sides of 2-d shapes*
A collection of 2-d shapes, a feely bag, counters
Place the shapes in the bag. The children take turns to pull out a shape and count the number of sides it has. They pick up a matching number of counters. The children check each other's counting. They have five turns each. Who collects the most counters?

ACTIVITY 2
2-3 children

- *Sorting 2-d shapes according to the shape of their sides*
- *Sorting objects with two non-distinct criteria*
Shape cards (PCMs 26, 27), two hoops, card for labels ('straight sides', 'curved sides')
Place the hoops on the table separately and place one label on each. Shuffle the cards and place them face down in a pile. The children take turns to reveal a card and place it in the correct hoop. If they have both straight **and** curved sides, they put them to one side.

ACTIVITY 3
3-4 children

- *Sorting 2-d shapes according to the shape of their sides*
Shape cards (PCMs 26, 27), counters
Spread out the cards face down on the table. The children take turns to reveal a card. According to the shape, they take one counter for straight sides only, two for curved sides only and three for straight and curved sides. The children continue until all the cards have gone. The winner is the player with the most counters.

ACTIVITY 4
2+ children

- *Sorting 2-d shapes according to the shape of their sides*
Infant game 22: 'Shape Maze', a blank dice or cube (labelled as shown below), counters
(See instructions on the card.)

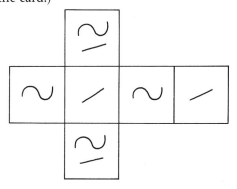

ACTIVITY 5
3-4 children

- *Classifying shapes according to the shape of their sides*
- *Naming common 2-d shapes*
- *Counting the number of sides of 2-d shapes*
A collection of 2-d shapes, a feely bag
Place the shapes in the bag. The children take turns to feel a shape and describe its sides, e.g. *All straight, all curved, straight and curved*. After they have described it, they remove it from the bag to check if they were correct. They try to say how many sides it has, and name the shape.

S5 **3-d shape**

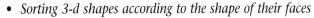

ACTIVITY 1
Whole class, then 3-4 children

- *Sorting 3-d shapes according to the shape of their faces*
- *Predicting and exploring if 3-d shapes will roll*

A set of 3-d shapes, a feely bag, a board (for a slope)
Place the shapes in the bag. The children take turns to feel for a shape, and predict whether it will roll down the hill or not. They remove it and test it, then describe the faces on the shapes.

ACTIVITY 2
3-4 children

- *Sorting 3-d shapes according to the shape of their faces*
- *Naming the faces of a 3-d shape*
- *Sorting objects with two non-distinct criteria using a Venn diagram*

A set of 3-d shapes, card for labels ('flat faces', 'curved faces'), two hoops, a feely bag
Place the hoops on the table so they intersect, and place one label on each hoop. Place the shapes in the feely bag. The children take turns to remove a shape and place it in the correct position inside the hoops.

ACTIVITY 3
3-4 children

- *Sorting 3-d shapes according to the shape of their faces*

A collection of classroom objects
The children collect a set of objects from around the classroom, some of which have flat faces only, some of which have curved faces only and some of which have both flat and curved faces. They sort the objects into groups and draw each group.

ACTIVITY 4
3-4 children

- *Sorting 3-d shapes according to the shape of their faces*
- *Naming the faces of a 3-d shape*

A set of 3-d shapes, a feely bag, counters
Place the shapes in the bag. The children take turns to feel for a shape, then remove it. If it has flat faces only, they take one counter; curved faces only, two counters; both flat and curved faces, three counters. They try to name the shape of some of the faces. When all the shapes have been removed, the winner is the player who has collected the most counters.

S6 Position

ACTIVITY 1
Whole class, in pairs

- *Recognising the positions above, below and beside*
Interlocking cubes (variety of colours – similar piles for each pair)
Give instructions to build towers or models, using the words above, below and beside. E.g. *start with a blue cube. Put a red cube above it. Put a yellow cube below the blue. Put a pink beside the red.*

ACTIVITY 2
2 children

- *Recognising the positions above (below and beside)*
Three sets of number cards (0 to 9) (PCM 3), counters (one colour per child)
Shuffle two of the sets of cards and arrange them in a 5 x 4 grid, face up. Shuffle the third set and place it in a pile face down. The children take turns to take a card from the pile and find a matching number on the grid. They place a counter on a card which is 'above' that number, or on the table above if it is the top row. When all the cards have been taken, reshuffle them to make a new pile. The children continue until all the cards in the middle two rows have a counter. Who placed the most? Extend the activity by asking the children to place counters below or beside the number on each card turned up.

ACTIVITY 3
2 children

- *Recognising the positions above, below and beside*
Number cards (2 to 10) (PCM 3), card for labels ('above', 'below', 'beside'), number grid 2 (PCM 14), counters (one colour per child)
Shuffle the cards, and lay them face down in a pile. The children take turns to choose a label, then turn over a card, e.g. they choose 'below', and draw card 4. They look at the grid and place a counter directly below the actual number on the grid. The children continue taking turns, reshuffling the cards, until one child has a line of three counters.

ACTIVITY 4
Pairs

- *Following instructions (above, below and beside) for building a model*
Interlocking cubes (a variety of colours), book or card
The children place a book or barrier between them. One child makes a simple model using six cubes without their partner seeing. She describes how to build it using the words 'above', 'below' and 'beside', and naming the colours. Her partner builds the model according to her instructions and then they check – the two models should be identical. Repeat, swapping roles.

ACTIVITY 5
Pairs

- *Following positional instructions*
KidPix or similar drawing package (create a file which contains objects)
The children must follow instructions (either recorded in KidPix or task cards) to place new objects in the correct positions on a picture. E.g. *put the sun above the house, put the tree beside the house*, etc.

S7 # Symmetry

ACTIVITY 1
Whole class, or 2+ children

- *Creating symmetrical pictures*
- *Completing a symmetrical picture, given one side of the picture*

Paper, pencils, scissors, paints, paintbrushes

The children design a symmetrical face with a hat on. They fold their piece of paper, open it out and draw half of the face on one side of the fold line. They refold the paper so that the outline of the face is visible, cut around the outline and then open it out. The children then complete the drawing of the face, making sure that it is symmetrical. Finally, they paint one side of the face, quickly, before folding the paper shut again. They press on the paint and then open out the paper to reveal the face coloured on both sides. (For a whole class activity use crayons and colour pencils rather than paints.)

ACTIVITY 2
2+ children

- *Creating symmetrical patterns*
- *Locating the line of symmetry in a symmetrical pattern*

A collection of different shaped leaves, paint or ink, paper, pencils, rulers

The children make leaf-prints. When the paint is dry, they draw the lines of symmetry on the leaves.

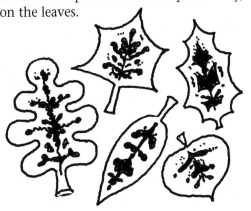

ACTIVITY 3
2+ children

- *Creating symmetrical patterns*

Paint (several colours), paper

The children fold a sheet of paper in half, open it up and make a paint-blot pattern on one side of the fold line. They fold the two halves together, pressing gently, and open it out to create a pattern with symmetry.

ACTIVITY 4
2+ children

- *Creating symmetrical pictures*
- *Completing a symmetrical picture, given one side of the picture*

Magazines, mirror, paper, glue, scissors

The children fold a piece of paper in half and then open it out. They cut out a half-picture from a magazine and stick it next to the fold line on the paper. They draw the other side of the picture on the blank side of the fold line to match the half-picture so that the finished picture is symmetrical. Suggest that they use the mirror to help them with the drawing.

D1 Sorting

ACTIVITY 1
Whole class, then 3-4 children

- *Sorting objects into two distinct non-intersecting sets*
Cubes of four different colours (blue, red, yellow, green), card for labels ('red', 'yellow', 'blue', 'green'), two hoops, a feely bag
The children choose two of the labels, and place them on the hoops. The cubes are placed in the bag. The children take turns to draw a cube from the bag, and place it in the correct position, i.e. inside one of the hoops or outside both hoops. Let the children repeat the activity, choosing different pairs of labels.

ACTIVITY 2
3-4 children

- *Sorting objects into two distinct non-intersecting sets*
A set of playing cards, two hoops, card for labels ('black' and 'red', 'picture card' and 'not a picture card', 'heart' and 'diamond')
The hoops are put on the table and the children label them with one of the pairs of labels. They work together to sort the playing cards using the hoops. They check that they are correct and then move on to the next pair of labels.

ACTIVITY 3
3-4 children

- *Sorting objects into two distinct non-intersecting sets*
A set of 2-d shapes (3-, 4- or 5-sided), card for labels ('3 sides', '4 sides', '5 sides'), two hoops, a feely bag
The hoops are placed on the table. The children choose two of the labels and place them on the hoops. The shapes are placed in the bag. The children take turns to draw a shape from the bag and place it in the correct position, i.e. inside one of the hoops or outside both hoops. Let the children repeat the activity, choosing two different labels.

ACTIVITY 4
3-4 children

- *Sorting objects into two distinct non-intersecting sets*
- *Sorting objects into two non-distinct intersecting sets*
Attribute blocks (e.g. Logiblocs), card for labels ('thick' and 'thin', 'large' and 'small', 'blue' and 'red', 'square' and 'circle'), two hoops, a feely bag
The hoops are placed on the table. The children choose two of the labels and place them on the hoops. The blocks are placed in the bag. The children take turns to draw a block from the bag, and place it in position, i.e. inside one of the hoops or outside both hoops. Let the children repeat the activity, choosing different pairs of labels. Extend the activity to include sorting intersecting sets, e.g. 'large' and 'red'. Arrange the hoops so that they overlap and discuss which blocks can go in the intersection.

D2 **Sorting**

ACTIVITY 1
Whole class, then 3-4 children

• *Sorting numbers into two distinct non-intersecting sets*
Number cards (1 to 10) (PCM 3), two hoops, card for labels ('more than 6' and 'less than 6', 'less than 3' and 'between 4 and 9', 'odd' and 'even')
The hoops are placed on the table. The children label the hoops with one of the pairs of labels. They work together to sort the cards in the hoops. They check that they are correct and then move on to the next pair of labels.

ACTIVITY 2
3-4 children

• *Sorting numbers into two distinct non-intersecting sets*
A set of dominoes, two hoops, card for labels ('more than 8 spots' and 'less than 7 spots', 'less than 5 spots' and 'between 5 and 9 spots', 'both sides odd' and 'both sides even')
The hoops are placed on the table. The children choose one of the pairs of labels and place them on the hoops. They work together to sort the dominoes in the hoops. They check that they are correct and then move on to another pair of labels.

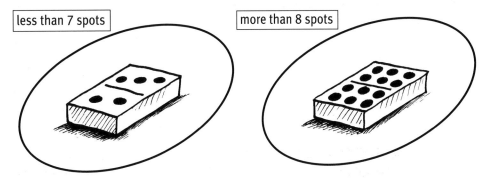

less than 7 spots   more than 8 spots

ACTIVITY 3
3-4 children

• *Sorting numbers into two distinct non-intersecting sets*
Coins (1p, 2p, 5p, 10p, 20p, 50p, £1, £2), card for labels ('silver' and 'bronze', 'more than 50p' and 'less than 50p', 'less than 20p' and 'more than 50p'), two hoops
The hoops are placed on the table. The children label the hoops with one of the pairs of labels. They work together to sort the coins in the hoops. They check that they are correct and then move on to another pair of labels.

ACTIVITY 4
3-4 children

• *Sorting numbers into two distinct non-intersecting sets*
• *Sorting numbers into two non-distinct intersecting sets*
Number cards (1 to 20) (PCMs 3, 4), two hoops, card for labels (e.g. 'more than 12' and 'less than 7')
The hoops are placed on the table. The children label them with one of the pairs. They work together to sort the cards in the hoops, checking that they are correct. Extend the activity to include sorting intersecting sets, e.g. 'more than 7' and 'less than 12'. Arrange the hoops so that they overlap and discuss which numbers can go in the intersection.

D3 Block graphs

ACTIVITY 1
Whole class, then 3-4 children

• *Constructing and interpreting a block graph*
A dice, blank block-graph sheet (PCM 29)
The children throw the dice 10 times and keep a score of how many times each number is thrown. They draw a block graph based on the results. Put the dice totals along the bottom of the graph. What does the graph show?

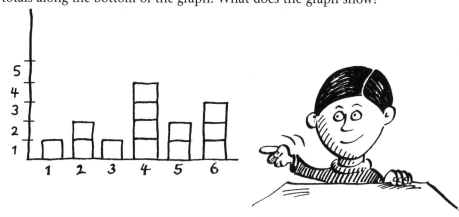

ACTIVITY 2
3 children

• *Constructing and interpreting a block graph*
Blank block-graph sheet (PCM 29)
The children work together to collect 15 classmate's names. They draw a block graph showing how many names have each number of letters. Put number of letters along the bottom of the graph. What does the graph show?

ACTIVITY 3
3-4 children

• *Constructing and interpreting a block graph*
Playing cards, blank block-graph sheet (PCM 29)
Shuffle the cards and deal out 15. The children draw a block graph to show how many there are of each suit (hearts, clubs, diamonds, spades). What does the graph show?

ACTIVITY 4
3-4 children

• *Constructing and interpreting a block graph*
• *Comparing two block graphs*
Cubes or counters (in four or five different colours), a feely bag, blank block-graph sheet (PCM 29), coloured pencils
Place the cubes in the bag. The children remove 20 cubes, one at a time. They draw a block graph to show how many there are of each colour. What does the graph show? Let them repeat the activity, taking another 20 cubes. This time, ask them to construct a block graph using the cubes as blocks and to build towers with them. Then let them copy the result onto the blank graph sheet. What does this graph show? Let them compare the two block graphs.

ACTIVITY 5
Pairs

• *Entering data to create a graph*
Appropriate spreadsheet software or graphing package, 120 cubes (five colours of random amounts)
The children record how many of each colour cube there are onto a simple graphing package or a spreadsheet previously set up by the teacher to generate a block graph.

D4 Pictographs

ACTIVITY 1
Whole class, or 6-7 children

• *Constructing and interpreting a pictograph*
Blank pictograph sheet (PCM 28)
The children find out how many brothers and sisters (including step-brothers and step-sisters) they each have. They draw a pictograph, with pin-people, showing how many children have no brothers and/or sisters, how many have one etc. They must make sure that the pin-people drawings are lined up underneath each other. (For the purposes of the pictograph, they need not distinguish between brothers and sisters, i.e. two brothers and one sister count as three.)

ACTIVITY 2
3-4 children

• *Constructing and interpreting a pictograph*
Blank pictograph sheet (PCM 28), playing cards
Shuffle the cards and deal out 10. The children draw a pictograph to show how many of each suit there are (hearts, clubs, diamonds, spades). For each picture on the graph they draw a small card.

ACTIVITY 3
3-4 children

• *Constructing and interpreting a pictograph*
Blank pictograph sheet (PCM 28)
The children draw a pictograph to show the number of letters in children's names. They collect a list of children's names (at least 20, or the whole class). They decide on what picture to use to represent a child, and then draw the key. They write the numbers of letters down the side of the sheet. What does the pictograph show?

ACTIVITY 4
4-5 children

• *Constructing and interpreting a pictograph*
• *Collecting and sorting a set of data*
Picture books, blank pictograph sheet (PCM 28)
The children conduct a survey of some of the picture books in the class. They can categorise them under the following headings: about animals, about life at home, about space, fairy-stories, funny stories, about monsters. Let them decide any other categories they need. The children draw a pictograph with a small picture of a book representing each real book. Which sort of picture book is most common?

D5 Sorting

ACTIVITY 1
3-4 children

• *Constructing and interpreting a table*
Playing cards (excluding the picture cards), a 4-column table drawn on A3 paper
Ask the children to draw or write the headings 'heart', 'club', 'diamond', 'spade'. Shuffle the cards and place 20 of them face down in a pile. The children take a card, one at a time, and decide in which column it belongs. They write the card number in the table. They continue until all the cards have been taken. Discuss what the table shows.

ACTIVITY 2
3-4 children

• *Constructing and interpreting a table*
Number cards (0 to 9) (PCM 3), a 3-column table drawn on A3 paper
Shuffle the cards and spread them out, face down. Write the headings 'straight lines', 'curved lines' and 'straight and curved lines' in the table. The children take a number card, one at a time, and decide if the number is constructed from straight lines, curved lines or both. They write the number in the matching column. Discuss what the table shows.

ACTIVITY 3
3-4 children

• *Constructing and interpreting a table*
Card for labels ('one', 'two' … 'ten')
Ask the children to label the headings '3 letters', '4 letters', '5 letters'. Shuffle the cards and place them face down in a pile. The children take turns to reveal a card, count its number of letters, then write the number in the correct column. When the table is complete, the children discuss the results.

ACTIVITY 4
3-4 children

• *Constructing and interpreting a table*
A set of dominoes, a 3-column table drawn on A3 paper
Ask the children to draw or write the headings 'less than 6 spots', '6 spots', and 'more than 6 spots'. Spread out ten dominoes, face down. The children take turns to reveal a domino, decide to which column it belongs, then draw a picture of the domino in its appropriate column. When the table is complete, discuss the results. Let the children repeat the activity for a different selection of ten dominoes.

ACTIVITY 5
3-4 children

• *Constructing and interpreting a table*
• *Collecting and recording a set of data*
The children draw a table to show how many letters there are in each of the names of the children in the class. They start by making a list of the names, decide how many columns they need, write headings for the columns, and put the names in their appropriate column. Ask the children to choose a title for the table. Discuss the results. Extend this activity by altering the title headings, e.g. 'less than 5 letters' 'between 5 and 8 letters', 'more than 10 letters' or repeat with a different class and compare the results.

Glue here

| 1 | 2 | 3 4 | 5 | 6 | 7 | 8 | 9 | 10 |
| 11 | 12 | 13 14 | 15 | 16 | 17 | 18 | 19 20 |

Glue here

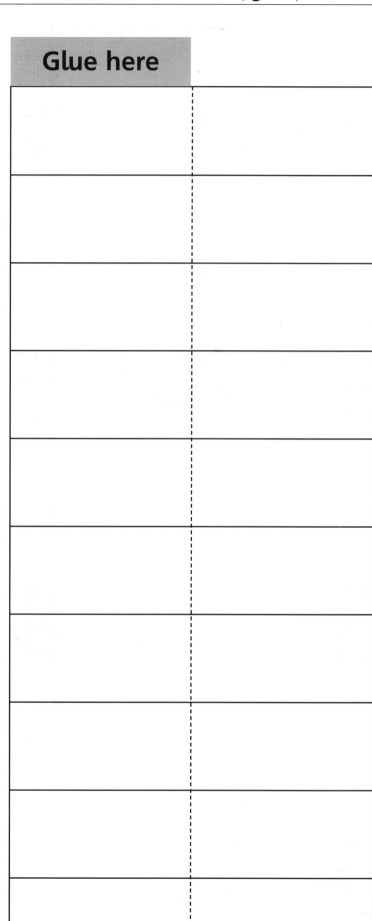

0	1	2
3	4	5
6	7	8
9	10	

15	20
14	19
13	18
12	17
11	16

21	**22**	**23**	**24**
25	**26**	**27**	**28**
29	**30**	**31**	**32**
33	**34**	**35**	**36**

37	38	39	40
41	42	43	44
45	46	47	48
49	50	51	52

53	**54**	**55**	**56**
57	**58**	**59**	**60**
<u>**61**</u>	**62**	**63**	**64**
65	<u>**66**</u>	**67**	<u>**68**</u>

69	**70**	**71**	**72**
73	**74**	**75**	**76**
77	**78**	**79**	**80**
81	**82**	**83**	**84**

85	**86**	**87**	**88**
89	**90**	**91**	**92**
93	**94**	**95**	**96**
97	**98**	**99**	**100**

50 40	30	20	10
100 90	80	70	60

45	95
35	85
25	75
15	65
5	55

3	3	2	6
6	1	5	4
2	2	5	2
3	7	1	8

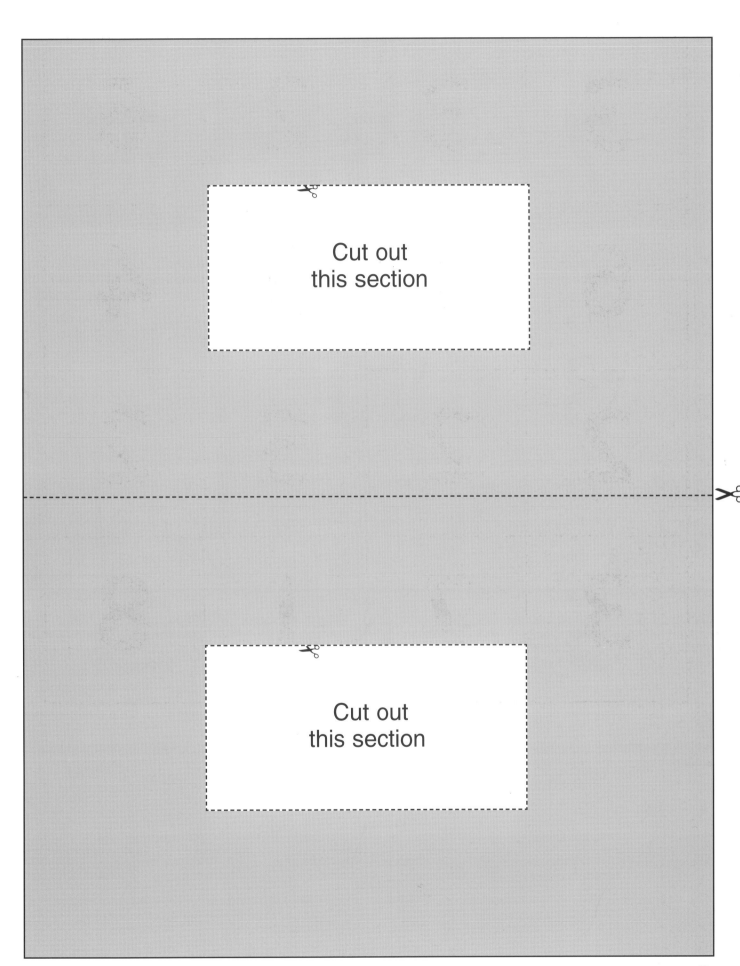

Cut out
this section

Cut out
this section

7	3	q
8	l0	4
5	6	2

15	12	17
19	20	14
13	16	18

0	1	2	3	4
5	6	7	8	9
10	11	12	13	14
15	16	17	18	19
20	21	22	23	24
25	26	27	28	29
30	31	32	33	34
35	36	37	38	39

1	2	3	4	5	6	7	8	9	10
11	12	13	14	15	16	17	18	19	20
21	22	23	24	25	26	27	28	29	30
31	32	33	34	35	36	37	38	39	40
41	42	43	44	45	46	47	48	49	50
51	52	53	54	55	56	57	58	59	60
61	62	63	64	65	66	67	68	69	70
71	72	73	74	75	76	77	78	79	80
81	82	83	84	85	86	87	88	89	90
91	92	93	94	95	96	97	98	99	100

first	second	third
fourth	fifth	sixth
seventh	eighth	ninth
tenth		

1st	2nd	3rd
4th	5th	6th
7th	8th	9th
10th		

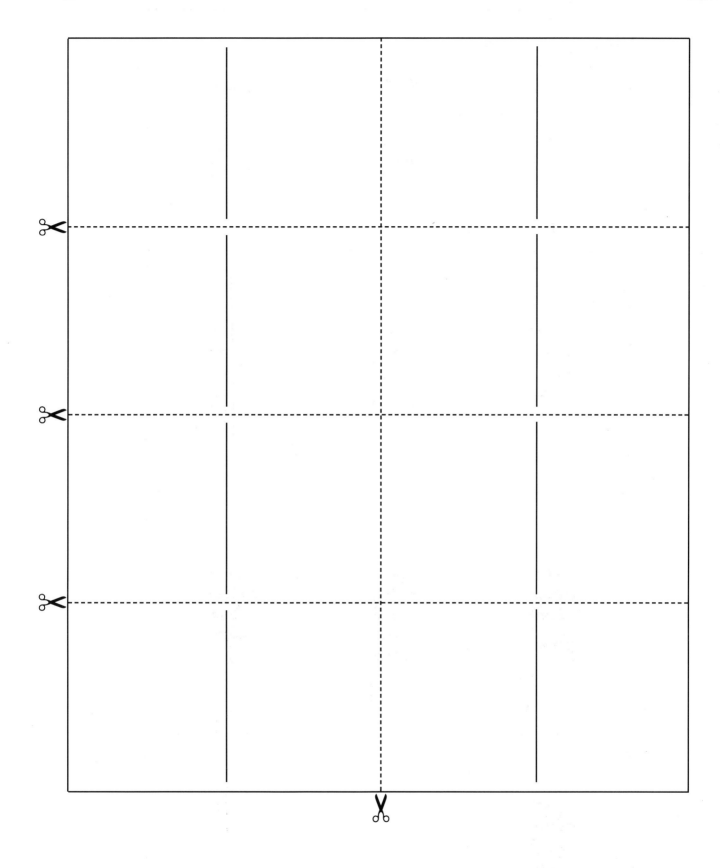

Clock-face sheet

1

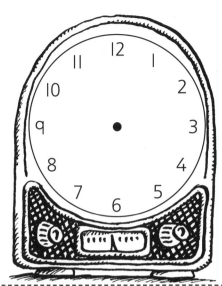

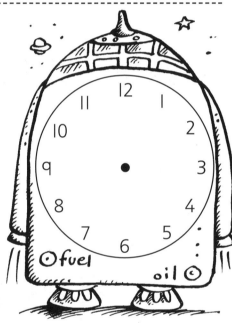

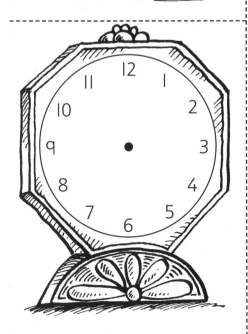

Monday

Tuesday

Wednesday

Thursday

Friday

Saturday

Sunday

86

February	April	June
January	March	May

88

August	July
October	September
December	November

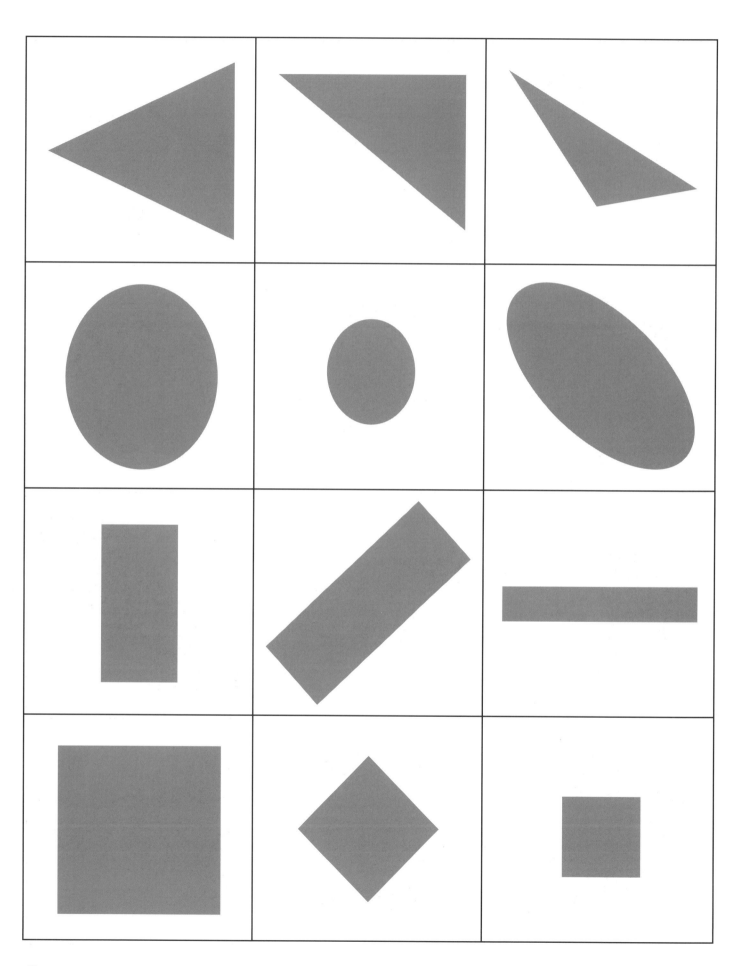

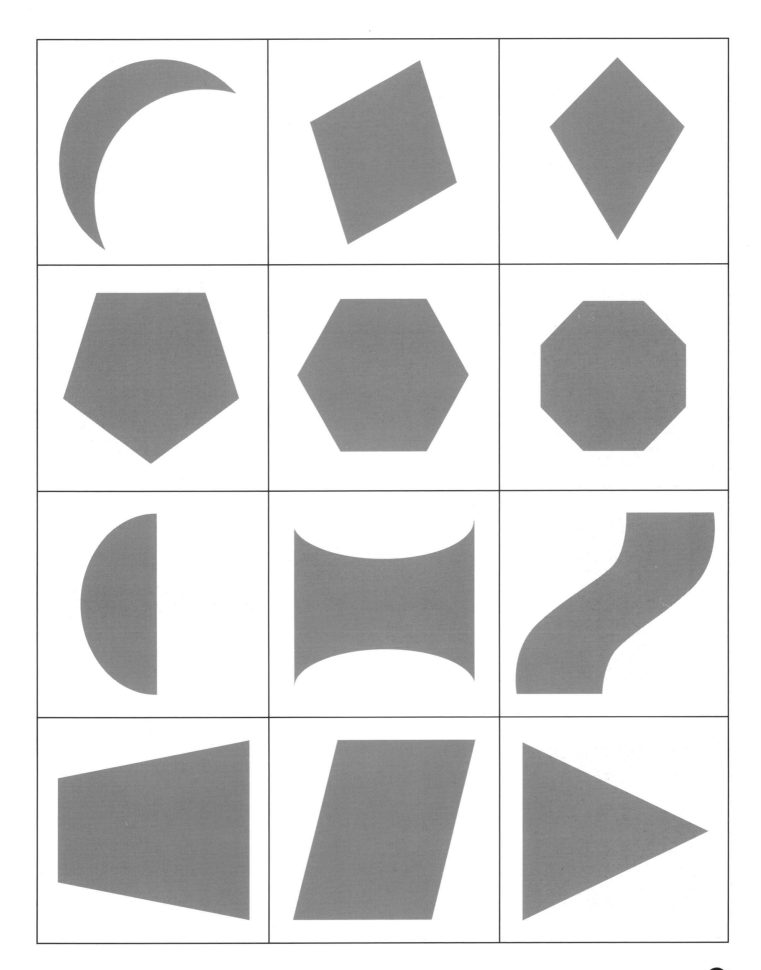

title:

key:

Teacher's Instructions

(Teacher/pupil input: Give your pictograph a title. Label the rows on the left. Draw your key and complete your pictograph.)

title:

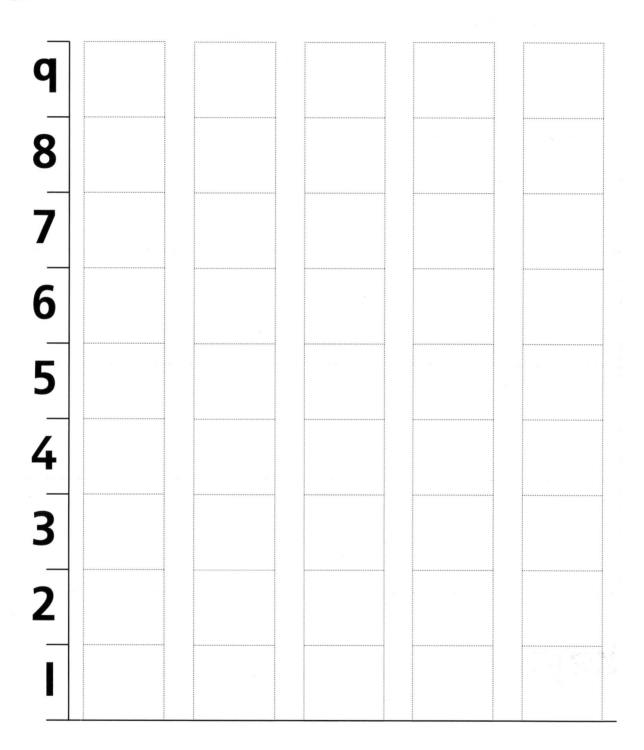